A Special Stretch of Sky

A Special Stretch of Sky

Selected Works
from the
COMPAS Writers & Artists in the Schools Program

Edited by
John Coy

Illustrations by
Eva Two Crow

COMPAS
Writers & Artists in the Schools
1997

Publication of this book is generously supported by the Lillian Wright and C. Emil Berglund Foundation, dedicated in memory of C. Emil Berglund.

COMPAS programs are made possible in part by grants provided by the Minnesota State Arts Board, through an appropriation by the Minnesota State Legislature. In the past year, the COMPAS Writers & Artists in the Schools program has received generous support from the Hugh J. Andersen Foundation, the Ashland Oil Foundation, the Lillian W. & C. Emil Berglund Foundation, Josten's Foundation, Land O'Lakes Foundation, Medtronics Foundation, Ronald McDonald Children's Charities and the First Bank System Foundation.

As always, we are grateful for the hundreds of excellent teachers throughout Minnesota who sponsor COMPAS Writers & Artists in the Schools residencies. Without their support and hard work, the writers and artists would not weave their magic, and the student work we celebrate in this book would not spring to life.

Book Production: Arah Bahn, WAITS Program Associate
Daniel Gabriel, WAITS Program Director

Book Design: Arah Bahn

ISBN 0-927663-30-9

COMPAS
304 Landmark Center
75 West Fifth Street
St. Paul, Minnesota 55102

Jeff Prauer, Executive Director
Daniel Gabriel, Director, Writers & Artists in the Schools

TABLE OF CONTENTS

TABLE OF CONTENTS

TABLE OF CONTENTS

TABLE OF CONTENTS

INTRODUCTION

Each year thousands of Minnesota students have the opportunity to work with visiting writers who invite them to try new things and look at the world in new ways. The writer comes into a school with no knowledge of who likes to write and who does not, so each student is given a fresh start. The students write about their experiences, their fears and their hopes. They write and rewrite and write again. They take their stories and poems home and write some more.

The cooperation and support of many people are necessary for a successful residency. Teachers, administrators, librarians, parents, and community members work to provide funding and planning and generate enthusiasm. Visiting writers come into the school with energy and commitment. And then the students dive in and create the songs and poems and stories that we are fortunate to hear.

The title of this anthology and all of the section titles come from the writing of students. Laura Martell in her poem "Just My Theory" encourages us to "dream the dreams we haven't dreamed" and reminds us that "each of us has a special stretch of sky." In the pages of this book you are invited to visit the special stretch of sky of some fine young writers.

In "The First Poem" Paula Smith says, "The first poem was created by rocks. They fell down in rhythm and make a beautiful sound." The poets and writers before you use rhythm and beautiful sounds in their pieces about the natural world, animals, memories, daily life, emotions and dreams. Whether writing about a trombone, a peanut, mittens, sunsets, tornadoes, a favorite pig, the crack of a wooden baseball bat, the Menard's man, the barn on the farm, or yellow cone flowers, these young writers use fresh images and surprising connections to describe what they see.

Making the selections for this anthology is always a challenging task. Students provide visiting writers with many interesting stories, songs and poems. Of these the writers choose five for each week of residency work that reflect the imagination and depth of work created in residencies. Due to considerations of variety and space, many excellent pieces have not been included, and the writing in *A Special Stretch of Sky* represents the work of thousands of students throughout the state.

The art on the cover and section pages was created by Eva Two Crow and we are fortunate to have her images be a part of this book.

In the last poem of this volume Phillip Martini begins "I am the child of imagination" and we remember that is how we all began. Phillip describes walking in the desert and seeing a man. "He gives me something. It looks like a key. I unlock the door and it leads to me."

This search and discovery is the essence of the residency process. Children of imagination go exploring and are occasionally presented with a key. As adults we are reminded how important these keys are and what an honor it is to present a young person with one.

"I unlock the door and it leads to me."

Welcome to the twentieth annual COMPAS anthology, a celebration of student writing in Minnesota.

John Coy
July 1997

A NOTE TO TEACHERS

USING *A Special Stretch of Sky*
AS SOURCE MATERIAL FOR WRITING

This year's COMPAS anthology, *A Special Stretch of Sky*, celebrates the work done by Minnesota students participating in the 1996-97 Writers & Artists in the Schools (WAITS) program. This book also can serve as a valuable teaching tool. Students are impressed, encouraged and stimulated when they listen to and read the writing of their peers.

You will find vivid examples of writing here that you might use to inspire your own students to write. Certain poems, stories or plays may speak to you in a special way. Note them. Imagine how you might write a similar poem or story. Examine the writing to discern what technique, narrative, metaphor or idea helped the student shape his or her experience into that poem or story.

You might select your own subject and have students write similes and images defining it. Trying to figure out how certain poems were written may be more difficult. Ask yourself, how did the student write this poem? Where did they start? Perhaps you have only a hunch, but try writing a similar one yourself. This will help clarify the underlying structure and inspiration that motivated the student to write his or hers. The model poem and the one you write will provide two fine examples that you can present to the class. Students are always thrilled and especially encouraged when their teachers share their own writing with them.

COMPAS writers and artists who come to your school to teach are also excellent resources for new ideas. Most will gladly give you additional ideas you can use to inspire your students. Finally, just letting your students page through this book is valuable as well. Let them read work by writers like themselves, so they will see and believe that not only is such writing possible, it is also important.

The First Poem

The first poem was created by
rocks.
They fell down in rhythm
and made a beautiful
sound.
The sound was like music
landing on the ground
and made a big hole
that is now
the Grand Canyon.

Paula Smith, Grade 4
LeCenter Elementary School, LeCenter
Writer-in-Residence: Sigrid Bergie

THE EARTH'S BODY

Earth

Fog, rain, sleet, snow . . .
All this weather on the Earth.
Mountains so high.
What if it were true?
The table walks! Stop the table!
A dinosaur or two together as one.
Face, hands, arms, legs . . .
All these people. . . .
Your room raining walls
that taste like ice cream.
Fingers like lollipops.
The Earth's body
feeling all this
in one world.
You tell me,
one thousand streets,
evil factories,
and a math problem:
one thousand and twenty-two
times one million
equals
I don't know. . . .
So I wave the flags and quit,
good-bye forever.

Ashley Kern, Grade 4
Middleton Elementary School, Woodbury
Writer-in-Residence: Carol Dines

Inside This Shell

Inside this shell
is heaven and beyond.
It sings a song
a song of birds,
a song of the sky.
It travels the world
with wonder, with no idea.
For it is silent, and with
no motion, but it travels
with the blue sea
and with the sun.

Inside this shell is a
shooting star. A world
of thought. A world of
animals, a world of
peace.

Inside this shell
is the wind,
the trees,
the flowers,
the rain.

Inside this shell
is an unknown world
a world where I
will return again.

Jessica Santos, Grade 4
Fulton Community School, Minneapolis
Writer-in-Residence: Sheila O'Connor

Stars

I am waiting, waiting
for the stars. The stars that are
like sparkling ideas. Sometimes
they are there and sometimes
they leave you in the ditch
far away from home. The sun is setting
and I am sitting on the white beach.
As I listen to the soft lullaby
of the giant ocean, I stare up
to the sky and the faint sun
stares back as if to whisper, "Stay
awake." My eyes droop, I shake
my head to stay awake. The
ocean whispers, whispers, whispers.

Maren Searle, Grade 5
Tanglen Elementary School, Hopkins
Writer-in-Residence: John Minczeski

I Wonder

Looking up in the sky, I looked,
I stared, and I wondered.

I wondered what makes the soft
fluffy cloud move. I wonder
what's going on up there.

Is it when someone cries up there
so that it rains? Is it when someone
up there is happy and joyful, so today
is pretty and nice?

I wonder who or what changes these
seasons: winter that is so cold but fun
with snow, spring that is so cool
and nice, summer that is so hot but when
you jump in the water, "Ooh, it feels so nice,"
fall when the leaves have left the trees
and it starts all over again.

I've wondered why I wonder.

Yen Dang, Grade 6
Parkway Elementary School, Saint Paul
Writer-in-Residence: Roseann Lloyd

The Big Stream

Dear stream, when I
went over you I felt
I was in your stream.
You kept on going.
I felt like you were
my best friend and I
was the only one you
walked to. You were the
only person who wore
all blue. You were the
only person who stayed
wet and when somebody
would try to throw a towel
at your blue clothes the towel
would fall and keep falling and
it would be all wet and wouldn't
dry you. I was the only person
you would let swim in your
pockets and ride through your long
blue hair. I was the only person that
felt your cold wet skin.

Lashea Powell, Grade 6
Sheridan Elementary School, Saint Paul
Writer-in-Residence: Susan Marie Swanson

Untitled

The thunderstorm feels light as a feather
coming down the paths of the highway.

Nobody knows how it happens.

It sounds like a lion roaring
all the way from Chicago.

It smells like dark shredded roses
dancing in the wind.

And it tastes bitter as my tears
when people are mean to me.

Now it's rushing to be first
to water the plants—

Sunflowers, violets, chili peppers.

Nicole Beard, Grade 5
Eisenmenger Program/Museum Magnet School, Saint Paul
Writer-in-Residence: John Minczeski

I Am

I am a cardinal soaring through the air
as red as a rose. I am a rabbit hopping in the
snow, my footprints in the snow follow me.
I am the mist in the spring air. I am the sunshine
in the summer picnics. I am the blue of the
beautiful blueberries. I am the pink of paint
that sparkles on the house. I am the
silence of the kite soaring in air.
I am the silence of the wind when
it stops. I am the waterfall shining the rocks
below. I am the flower blooming in the
spring air. I am the stars in the sparkle
in the night.

Megann Class, Grade 3
Parkway Elementary School, Saint Paul
Writer-in-Residence: Dana Jensen

High in the Mountains

High in the mountains!
Up, up, up, up, down, down, down!
High in the mountains!
Up, up, up, up, down, down, down!

Verses

I'll pull you on a rope
Up, up, up, up, down, down, down
We'll wear our boots and coats
Up, up, up, up, down, down, down

We'll have lunch and a snack
Up, up, up, up, down, down, down
Carry it in our backpack
Up, up, up, up, down, down, down

We'll go hiking, and won't stop
Up, up, up, up, down, down, down
We plan to get to the top
Up, up, up, up, down, down, down

Ms. Reidell's Class, Grade 1
Parkway Elementary School, Saint Paul
Musician-in-Residence: Charlie Maguire

The Past Is Not Always Forgotten

My sweet, innocent climbing tree
you were always there for me
but soon you'll be gone.
Your leaves the color of sea foam
green and the sound of the wind
rustling them; faintly sounding like
a flute. . . I wished that it could
always be, but I know it cannot, for you,
like me, are a living thing.
We are allowed to sing for a time and
then we are destroyed, turned back into
grass. But I will never forget you, even
after they decapitate your regal soul with
the ax, like a blunt knife cutting in. . . .
I vow to keep you with me, perhaps as a
chair or a picture frame or a bowl to hold
oranges in.

Ann E. Gramstad, Grade 11
Elk River High School, Elk River
Writer-in-Residence: Margot Fortunato Galt

Tornadoes

Roaring like a lion
tearing houses apart,
the tornado, like the
swirl in your bath tub,
is taking things away—
houses, trees, cars, lives.

It comes in a green-black
sky glowing from inside.
It comes out of thunder, out
of hair, out of South Dakota.
It comes in a fingernail pointing down,
it comes in swirling branches,
sticks, trucks full of gas, teddy bears.

It has a taste for tearing things apart,
for throwing things
against shoe stores, apartments,
restaurants. It throws bricks
through walls. As it passes,
wood falls from the sky
like rain.

Pierre Glass, Grade 5
Eisenmenger Program/Museum Magnet School, Saint Paul
Writer-in-Residence: John Minczeski

Untitled

What is poetry?
Not the wind but the flutter of the wind
rustling silver leaves as it goes by.

What is poetry?
Not the sun but the yellow glitter over
the sea, not the cloud but the fluffy image
the cloud forms, not the flower but the
sweet yellow nectar, and not the bee but the
flying basket of honey.

Kevin Berg, Grade 5
Alice Smith Elementary School, Hopkins
Writer-in-Residence: Dana Jensen

The River Rising

The river rising,
Ever so slowly rising.
Like a lion
Creeping up on its prey.

Fat as a hippo.
Deep as a giraffe is tall.

Lapping against the sandbags.
Trying to break free.

Invading homes.
Filling them with water.

The water keeps seeping
Up and up,
Higher and higher,
Until it passes the high water mark.

The raging river
Like a lion,
Like a hippo,
Like a giraffe,
Like an animal in a cage,
Like a burglar.

The river rising.
Like so many things.
Except a river.

Erica Greil, Grade 4
J. F. Kennedy Elementary School, Hastings
Writer-in-Residence: John Coy

Don't Go In The Mud

Said my Aunt, but we forgot.
My cousin and I were camping with her
and we were bored
so we ran into the mud anyway.
The faucet was placed over a patch of dirt
When we turned it on, it was like chocolate,
Melted chocolate gushing between our toes,
With each stomp we got even more dirty.
Quit it, you guys, you're going to have to shower again, she'd say.
I had mud in my eyes, mud on my face, mud everywhere, head to toe.
When we got tired of slipping, slushing, glacking around in the mud, we left
The mud began to dry before we could get to a shower.
It was caked on.
It was hard to move, our skin felt tight as a snare drum.
When we got cleaned up, we couldn't resist it.
Don't go back in the mud, she would say,
I'm not taking you back to the shower again. . . .
But we had to, it was calling us.
Mud again. Shower again.
All day.

Luke Dekarske, Grade 7
Oltman Junior High School, Saint Paul Park
Writer-in-Residence: Roseann Lloyd

Four Seasons

Refrain

Four seasons!
One, two, three, four!
Four seasons!
One, two, three, four!
We like the four seasons
Warm, hot, cold, and freezing
Four seasons!

Warm season in the springtime
Watch those flowers grow
Red, yellow, and purple
All blooming in a row, all blooming in a row

Hot season in the summer
To the beach we go
Or slugging out a home run
Going down to the show, going down to the show

Cold season in the fall
Watch those leaves fall down
Making beautiful colors
All over town, all over town

Freezing in the winter
Sliding down a hill
Don't crash into somebody
Or you'll take a spill, or you'll take a spill

Mr. Boesel's Class, Grade 3
Parkway Elementary School, Saint Paul
Musician-in-Residence: Charlie Maguire

Farm Morning

Every morning when I get up it's dark. I
get food for the animals and something
for the sun. I run a mile out to meet
the sun. I meet him and give him
what he wants: a gallon of
"dawn" paint that he paints
the sky with every
morning.

The sun paints the sky with careful streaks.
Lines of radiant yellow, blazes of atomic
red and different shades of pinks
and oranges. Then he hands the
bucket to me, picks up the
sunrise and brings it to
the museum of China.

Nicole Mjoness, Grade 5
Elm Creek Elementary School, Maple Grove
Writer-in-Residence: Dana Jensen

What I Love

The stars are what I love, glowing and glistening on a royal blue
quilt of dreams that is pulled over yesterday. I love a setting
sun that is a vanilla pudding with raspberry sauce, hiding
behind mountains of crystal sugar. The sea is my love, both
wild and calm, everlasting, as old as the stones that lie
shining at its ground, mirrors for the fish—and the mermaids.
I love tea that smiles at me, out of the carefully painted
stone mug till it warms me from the inside, just like the
smile in my best friend's eyes when we'll meet again at
the airport. I love chestnuts roasting over a fireplace that
brightens my living room like a fresh bouquet of wild flowers.
A letter in the mailbox with the most gentle handwriting on an
envelope, as fragile as a frozen daisy, makes me feel buoyant—
a roller coaster ride at midnight.

Svenja Nielsson, Grade 12
Roseau High School, Roseau
Writer-in-Residence: John Minczeski

ALL THE ANIMALS COMING BACK

The Riverbank

The river is like
a nice quiet place in the woods.
There's fresh fish, clean water, a waterfall
and some animals.
I see deer drinking,
squirrels hopping tree to tree,
a bear catching fish,
snakes looking for mice,
fish jumping, mice running,
and birds flying.
I see people coming.
All the animals disappear.
The people say
they just want to fish.
They catch about seven.
Then they go home.
I can hear all the animals
coming back from their hiding places
doing what they were doing before.

Eng Xiong, Grade 4
Franklin Music Magnet School, Saint Paul
Writer-in-Residence: John Coy

Cheetah

The cheetah looks for movement,
thinking of food. He moves his head
to the left and searches. He spots
a young antelope and lashes at it.
The baby listens and hears the cheetah
in the tall grass behind an old tree.
He runs. The baby antelope hears
and runs. The cheetah catches it
by running 70 miles per hour.
The next day he smells a mother rabbit
and hides and runs. The rabbit smells
him and runs, but the cheetah
catches her. She will never see another day.
That night I ran to the cheetah and
asked if he would come play with me.
That night we pranced and danced
and wrestled around. That night
I slept at his house and we laughed
making funny jokes. He told me
to be quiet because he heard
a lion hunting. The next day
he felt my hand rubbing his fur
and he woke. He taught me how to hide
and catch food. I went home
until we saw each other another day.

Anthony Belgarde, Grade 4
Bug-O-Nay-Ge-Shig School, Cass Lake
Writer-in-Residence: John Minczeski

Be Quiet, Foxes

Be quiet foxes.
You can get rabbits,
but be quiet.
You can get chickens,
but be quiet.
You can get rats,
but be quiet.
You can have baby
foxes, but be quiet.
You can have red
coats, but be quiet.
It is almost dawn, so
you should go to
sleep anyway.
All the other animals
are sleeping, so you will
not get any luck.

Anne Bergquist, Grade 1
Aquila Primary Center, Saint Louis Park
Writer-in-Residence: Susan Marie Swanson

The Lioness

Her eyes light up,
    She's found her prey
Its body is in sight
    When she sniffs the air
her breath
    Drinks up the light
her claws are silver stones
    She flies
and grabs it by the neck
    her teeth pull it down to deeper
dark
her paws red with
    blood
She licks them
her face turns toward the
moon
    and she drinks what
light is left

Asha Agar, Grade 6
Fulton Community School, Minneapolis
Writer-in-Residence: Dana Jensen

Salamander

Once upon a time in the deep jungle there lived a salamander. One day Salamander was walking and he saw his good friend Snake.

"Snake, I was thinking I'm too plain," said Salamander. "Should I wish to be brighter?"

"Oh no," said Snake. "Wish to have a tongue like mine."

Salamander thought a minute. "No thanks," he said. So Salamander went to see Parrot.

"Parrot, I hate being just orange and black. I'm too plain," said Salamander.

"Well, wish for a pair of wings like mine," said Parrot.

Salamander thought a minute. "Well, no." So Salamander went to see Monkey.

"Monkey, I want to be different, what should I do?" asked Salamander.

"Wish for a tail like mine," said Monkey.

Salamander thought for a minute. "Na," said Salamander. So Salamander went to see Lion.

"Lion, what should I wish for—a tongue like Snake, a pair of wings like Parrot, or a tail like Monkey?" asked Salamander.

"Well, a mane like mine is nice," said Lion.

Salamander thought a minute. "No way." So Salamander went to see Hippo.

"Hippo, could you help me figure out what to wish for?" asked Salamander.

"Of course, wish for teeth like mine," said Hippo.

Salamander thought a minute. "Too big for me, " he said. So Salamander went to see Elephant.

"Elephant, what should I wish for?" asked Salamander.

"A nose like mine would be fine," said Elephant.

Salamander thought a minute. "Too long," he said. So Salamander went to see Giraffe.

"Giraffe."

"Yes, Salamander."

"What should I wish for?" asked Salamander.

"A long neck like mine of course."

Salamander thought a minute. "Too long." So Salamander went to see Mole.

"Mole, what should I wish for, a tongue like Snake, a pair of wings like Parrot, a tail like Monkey, a mane like Lion, a nose like Elephant, or a neck like giraffe?" asked Salamander.

"None of those, wish for fur like mine," said Mole. Salamander thought a minute.

"Na." Then he went home for he had had a long rough day.

At home Salamander went over to his moss chair. There he thought and thought and thought and then he said, "I don't need a tongue, a tail, wings, a mane, a neck, a nose, teeth, or fur. I have all those, but in a salamander way."

Sheryl Robertson, Grade 4
North Hudson Elementary School, Hudson, Wisconsin
Writer-in-Residence: Stephen Peters

Connections

The willow tree droops down like
a pony's tail dropping to the ground.
As the pony trots over to meet
its owner, an apple for the pony.
The apple redder than a fire
in a house. As the house is burning,
the inside is hot. Hot as the day.
The pony is sweating so much
it looks like it just
came out of the freezer. The pony
looks like an ice cube.
Poor pony, I say to myself.
I jump onto the corral, I take
the pony to the shade. The pony
is not hot any more. My friend is coming.
"What are you doing," she says.
"Playing with my pony," I say.
"Can I play?" "Yes," I say.

Alexandra Helgeson, Grade 2
Saint Joseph's School, West Saint Paul
Writer-in-Residence: John Minczeski

Lucky and the Emerald Jewel

Once there was a dog named Lucky. His name was Lucky because when he was in a mess he got lucky. Lucky had to cross a moat to get to the emerald jewel. The jewel would heal all diseases. His master needed it. The trip was full of danger. There were unexpected traps. He set off. He wasn't even a quarter up the mountain when he heard a rumbling sound. He saw snow. It was an avalanche. He had to think fast! He jumped over the moving snow. "That was close!" he said. He kept on going. He was half way up the mountain and he smelled smoke. It was a wall of fire! He didn't know what to do. The fire was coming toward him! Soon he was back at the avalanche place. Down came the avalanche. He grabbed the snow, threw it at the fire, and put it out He ran until he came to the fire place. There was no fire. He was almost there when he saw a force field. He simply went around it. Then he saw the jewel. He lifted the case and slid down the mountain and returned to his master.

Kate Trenerry, Grade 2
Churchill Elementary School, Rochester
Writer-in-Residence: Stephen Peters

My Mind is a Frog

My mind is a frog waiting
for some flies and if
he gets one he will eat it all
up and if he eats it
he will jump and
dance and run and
he will fall asleep.

Derek Mathison, Grade 2
Chelsea Heights Elementary School, Saint Paul
Writer-in-Residence: Susan Marie Swanson

The Bear in the Spoon

One day a bear came upon a spoon. It was in the shrub. So the bear took it back to its cubs. They were going to have it for dinner. But the bears found out that they could not swallow the spoon. So the bear looked at the spoon and there was a little note that said, "Please say these words. They will make you rich with silver."

The bear said, "oh ha oh ha!"

Magically, the bear found himself surrounded by silver. He was so happy he forgot about his cubs. But when everything started to shake, he looked up and there were his cubs a million times bigger than him! Then it finally occurred to him that he was trapped in the spoon. But he got really scared when his cubs tried to push him into a railroad track. Of course, the cubs did not know what had happened so they had no use for the spoon and wanted to see it flattened. Then he got really scared. (Fortunately, the cubs were too late . . . the train had passed already.)

So, being as smart as he was he decided that if he said the words backwards he could maybe get out of the spoon.

"Ha ho, ha ho," and poof . . . he was back to normal. Then the bear buried the spoon.

Ben Yoder, Grade 4
Willow River Elementary School, Hudson, Wisconsin
Writer-in-Residence: Carol Dines

Untitled

Once upon a time there lived a mouse named Zach. He always wanted to be a crow so he could fly. When he was walking through the woods he saw bright light in a cave. Zach went and looked. It was a fairy. She was a magic fairy. The fairy said, "Hi how are you? You are the first one to find me."

Zach said, "Why?"

"The first animal who finds a fairy gets one wish. Zach you could pick a wish and I will grant it."

"How did you know my name?" Zach said.

"I'm a fairy."

"I wish I was a crow."

"Are you sure Zach?"

"Yes, I'm sure."

Then the fairy used her magic stick. So Zach got his wish. WOW!

"I'm a crow! Thank you fairy." When Zach flew over his house, everybody ran in the house because crows eat mice. Zach said, "WHY IS EVERYBODY RUNNING IN? I KNOW THEY'RE AFRAID OF ME." When Zach landed he was crying. Then Zach saw the fairy.

The fairy said, "Why are you crying?"

"Because everybody is scared of me. I want to be myself again." The fairy granted Zach his wish.

When Zach went home his mother said, "Zach Zach where have you been we have been looking all over for you. There was a big bird circling the house. Let's go inside."

Phoung Vu, Grade 4
Galtier Science/Mathematics Technology Magnet School, Saint Paul
Writer-in-Residence: Jovelyn Richards

Buck's Awesome Adventure

Boom! The speaker attached to Buck's 250 watt amplifier blew up. Buck was a normal dog, with black hair, living in a backwoods mansion on a lake. He had on his rad clothes and sunglasses and was throwing the biggest party this side of the universe. He had an okay stereo, but he wanted the biggest and baddest stereo around.

Buck was talking with Bob, Lucky, and Susan (his dog friends), about how to get a bigger stereo when it blew up. He tried frantically to fix it up, but it was hopeless. Buck said, "$300 down the drain. I can't believe it." "What are we going to do?" said Bob to Susan. "Man, if I only knew how to drive," Buck said. "Well, why don't we build up your bike to get your speakers," said Lucky. Yes! All day long they sat in the garage welding and building and soon they were done. They all got on. Everybody pedal! So they lifted off the ground, but not 10 feet away they dropped like a rock. "My tail," Buck said. "Oh well, I have to get going," said Lucky painfully.

Buck sat down in his Jacuzzi with a bandaged tail and thought I will just stay home. It is not worth it. Just as he said those words, Wondermutt sat down beside him and said, "Buck, think about it, don't you want the greatest stereo around?" You bet. So both of them thought his friends had given up on him. Now Wondermutt knew of the Cave Of Sound where the magical amplifiers were guarded by the evil cat centurion. Wondermutt said, "I will get you there, but you must enter alone. Remember the power of the milkbone is with you." Wondermutt disappeared in a cloud of smoke and Buck found himself in front of the Cave Of Sound.

He had to answer a riddle to get in. The gatekeeper was a centurion cat. The cat said, "If the maker doesn't want it, the buyer doesn't use it, and the user never sees it." Buck thought for a while. The cat said, "Well, I'm not getting any younger." Buck said calmly, "A coffin."

"You may pass." As soon as Buck entered, he was faced with many tasks that challenged him physically and mentally. He overcame them all and walked out of the Cave Of Sound with the magical amplifiers and speakers in hand. Wondermutt said, "Good job Buck."

Well, Buck hooked up his magical amplifiers and speakers and threw another party. This time it was a huge success and he was named TOP PARTY THROWER in all of the universe. Buck was revered as a hero from that day on.

Ken Scharpen, Grade 8
Zumbrota-Mazeppa Middle School, Mazeppa
Writer-in-Residence: Stephen Peters

A Good Pig

A pig smells nasty,
he lies in poop—a good pig,
a little, fat
good pig.
He jumps and flips—a good pig.
Oink, oink, he squeals
as I feed him slop.
He feels scared—his fuzzy body shakes.
He tastes good on the grill,
a good pig.

Amanda Yamry, Grade 4
Holdingford Elementary School, Holdingford
Writer-in-Residence: John Minczeski

Where's Dan Patch?

Refrain

Where's Dan Patch?
He's right here!
Where's Dan Patch?
He's right here!
He's in our school
He's in our town
Wherever you look, he's all around
Where's Dan Patch?
He's right here!

Where did he live?
The Taj Mahal!
Where did he live?
The Taj Mahal!
He lived in the Taj Mahal
With "onion domes" that were really tall
Where did he live?
The Taj Mahal!

What did he do?
He ran a race!
What did he do?
He ran a race!
At the old State Fair he ran a race
That famous horse took first place
What did he do?
He ran a race!

(Instrumental)
E, A, E, B,
E, A, E, B, E

How fast was he?

Really fast!
How fast was he?
Really fast!
Old Dan Patch, he was really fast
He ran on feed, he did not run on gas,
How fast was he?
Really fast!

Morning Core Group, Grade 4-6
M.W. Savage Elementary School, Savage
Musician-in-Residence: Charlie Maguire

LET'S TIPTOE BACK, SOFTLY NOW

Untitled

So you ask where I have been?
Do you dare to be hurled through black night
and then make a choice?
You will crouch in sharp-bladed grasses.
Where I have been is velvet smooth and poison.
Come, take this journey with me into silence
but this time I will walk with head held high
and I will give a mighty shout
to frighten the little girl in the back of the room.
No more will she haunt me in green and brown.
I know the last letter of every alphabet.
Let's tiptoe back, softly now, so as not to wake
the sleeping spectres of imaginary friends.
Listen to the lesson I have come here to learn—
about the metal of the earth . . . and fingertips.

Samantha Goodner, Grade 9
South View Middle School, Edina
Writer-in-Residence: Florence Dacey

Attic Room

Climbing up in silent darkness
on the creaking stair. The
door bursts open, I'm there.
In my house made of old
bookshelves and chests. I
am here in my house.
Time for the ball in my
most lovely dress. It's
real silk I think. Grandma's
old prom dress. I waltz with
a prince. My grandfather's
ventriloquist dummy. Hey
what's that? I'll have to
ask later. It may be a
treasure chest. I'm having so
much fun but now I'm so
busy. There are so many games
in my secret home.

Karen LeSuer, Grade 5
Meadowbrook Elementary School, Hopkins
Writer-in-Residence: Dana Jensen

The Magical Dancer

Here is my cousin Aryana
getting ready to
go to dance class.
She pictures herself spinning
like a flaming
fireball, leaping as high as a
flying dove.
Her dance costume has
magical heads banging
against each other, *ting ting*.
They sparkle like crystals
in the spotlight
of the evening. She looks
like a spinning beauty in
the old days trying
to win
the prince's heart over.
Her golden locket
bounces off of
her as she
spins, leaps,
and bows to the audience.

Janessa Vasquez, Grade 5
Sheridan Elementary School, Saint Paul
Writer-in-Residence: Susan Marie Swanson

My Grandma's Arms

Her door swings open,
her arms wide like a fur coat
ready to be wrapped
around my body.
She smells a musty smell
of happiness and loneliness,
a soothing smell like chicken soup
bubbling on the stove.
As I wiggle in her arms
and look into her rich coffee eyes,
they seem to be smiling on their own.
I stare at her face as her lips
wrinkle into a beautiful smile.
I sink back into her arms,
my body wrapped
in a shell of comfortable smells.
Her arms tighten around my body
as though she may never let me go.
Maybe I won't.

Siobhan Jones, Grade 9
Northfield High School, Northfield
Writer-in-Residence: Sigrid Bergie

The Barn on the Farm

In the field on the farm
petting the black cats
Riding the big red tractor.
Every time I come here, it thunders.
"Oh! You're getting so tall!"
Driving the red tractor in the bean field.
Fishin' with grandpa.
Their 50th Anniversary!
Packing the black lunch box
for grandpa.
Smell of the ham on Christmas
morning.
Big red tractor.
The mile long fields.
Driving the tractor.
Holding the kitties in my lap.
The big red tractor on the
farm near the barn.

Ian Martin, Grade 4
Christa McAuliffe Elementary School, Hastings
Writer-in-Residence: Margot Fortunato Galt

Here is my Family

Here is my dad making a mysterious bread in the breadmaker, the kind I do not know.

Here are my aunt, my uncle, and two cousins looking for sand dollars at the ocean.

Here are my grandpa and grandma making a chest for me for Christmas. My grandpa is making it out of wood, and my grandma is painting the design on it.

Here is my brother trying to read and watch the Super Bowl at once. Finally he gives up reading and starts watching just television.

Here is me. I am trying to read but my *other* brother (almost three years old) is trying to get me to play trucks and cars with him. Finally I give up reading and play with him.

Grace Vermeer, Grade 3
Fulton Community School, Minneapolis
Writer-in-Residence: Susan Marie Swanson

Every Detail, Every Petal

When I was a child, nothing could ever be simple. Even a drawing of my house could take days to draw. Everything had to be shaded, three dimensional and completely accurate along the lines of color and placement of objects before it could be considered finished. I always included every detail. This included my address, all of the surrounding houses, any signs, trees, gardens, and our Saint Bernard named Katie. I would draw every blade of grass, every petal on a tulip and even every single shingle.

In the fourth grade, my dog died. We gave our doghouse to our neighbors. One less box to draw, I thought, and so it was. Over time, the bird population in my pictures began to slowly diminish until there were none left. That year, there was a tornado. It took down three of our trees. I knew these had to be taken out of my pictures as well. Soon I decided not to spend my time drawing trees at all. Like a picture book, the clouds came through and slowly covered the sun. Then the fog set in. It began to cover everything until the whole picture faded away into nothing, along with my childhood.

Mark Tiefenbruck, Grade 9
Oltman Junior High School, Saint Paul Park
Writer-in-Residence: Richard Solly

Untitled

I remember his plaid jacket,
his comforting smile,
his big strong hands hugging me,
his dark skin,
his black hair,
his brown eyes,
and his daughter,
my sister, Carly.
My father,
who left notes in my jacket pocket
when I left his house.
My father
who I do not see anymore.

Darren Dexter, Grade 6
Hancock/Hamline Elementary School, Saint Paul
Writer-in-Residence: Sheila O'Connor

Untitled

I love the smell
of sage—it takes me back
to when my cousin's mom
passed away. It takes me
back to when my family
was crying. It takes
me back to when I last
saw her lying in her casket.
It takes me back to when
I was crying myself.

Malerie LaRose, Grade 6
Bug-O-Nay-Ge-Shig School, Cass Lake
Writer-in-Residence: John Minczeski

The Fire

I was about twelve years old at the time, and still feeling self-conscious about my "transition" phase. Glasses, braces, and cropped bangs created my appearance. But I had one good thing going for me—I was wearing my new purple down coat. That coat was the first thing that I had ever gotten that wasn't a hand-me-down. I'd always worn somebody else's something, and that was always good enough, but my parents decided that it was time for me to get something nice of my own. I even got to go to the store and try on every single coat in sight, and just as I was about to give up, I found that coat. It was a perfect dark lavender color, with black sleeve endings, and a soft black cotton collar. It also had a soft, fluffy down lining that soothed my skin when I wore it. I was so proud of that coat, and swore up and down never to take it off. The girls that had never looked in my direction before, suddenly looked at me in a whole new light. I was cool, I was attractive, and I was wanted and liked. I was finally the person that I always dreamed of being.

I bounced into church that morning full of energy, thankful that the Advent season would soon be over, so that I could finally eat chocolate again. My class gathered around our usual table, and we took turns lighting the candles that interrupted the Advent wreath. Everything was going fine, until I accidentally leaned over to try to reach a marker, when all of the sudden my whole head went up in flames. I remember feeling the warmth against my neck, as the milliseconds flew by. Before I could struggle a scream, my teacher, Mrs. Mensink, was already in the process of clapping her hands around my illuminated hair. The fire was out, yet I was still terrified as I sat there as motionless as a mannequin. The other kids just stared at me bug-eyed, and I tried to ignore the stench that was slowly filling my nostrils. Then it happened, someone laughed. I was devastated. I couldn't escape fast enough.

Mary Anne Snyder, who was in her car waiting for her kids to get done with Sunday school, saw me sprint from the building. She was our neighbor, and often watched my siblings and me when our parents were gone. Mary Anne had always been gentle and loving with me, and looked out for me as if I were her own daughter. As soon as she leaped from her car, and grabbed me from behind, she recognized the fear in my eyes. She slowed my sobs, by soothing me with her voice. When she finally got out of me what happened, she gathered me into her arms, gave me a quick hug, and promised me a quick ride home—straight to my mom.

I went into the door sobbing, and trying to reach for the locks of hair that just crumbled, scorched, into my tear-covered hands. My mom took one look at me, and immediately dropped her ironing and ran over to me. She gave me a big hug, and sweetly said, "Honey it's all right, everything's okay, just calm down." I relaxed in her arms.

I ended up having to get about four inches of burnt hair cut off, and I couldn't sleep for days. I just kept smelling that awful stench, and no matter how many times I scrubbed myself, I just couldn't seem to erase the odor, or memory from my mind. I never wore that purple coat that meant so much to me again. I was convinced that it was cursed. To this day, it still smells like the time my hair caught fire. Sure I can laugh now, I even find it kind of humorous. But when I look back, I still feel sad for that ugly, quiet, self-conscious little girl.

Emily Colbenson, Grade 11
Rushford-Peterson High School, Rushford
Writer-in-Residence: Stephen Peters

Snowman

I'll make a snow-man big and round
I'll make it tall,
I'll make a snow-man big and round
with three snow balls.

I'll use a banana for a mouth
A carrot for a nose.
I'll use buttons for the eyes
And a scarf and a hat for clothes.

Miss Lundquist's A.M. Class, Kindergarten
Parkway Elementary School, Saint Paul
Musician-in-Residence: Charlie Maguire

The Orange Cave

One day I was playing on the swingset. I tried to climb up the slide, but I couldn't. Then I heard something behind the trees. I hurried behind the trees. I saw a cave. The cave wasn't gray like most caves. The cave was orange! Each door was labeled with a title of a story. Except one. I went inside the door. A sign above a desk said PLEASE WRITE A STORY.

There was an apple next to the paper. It smelled delicious. I ate the apple. It was good. I wrote a story about a little girl named Kenna who wanted to find a friend. Suddenly I felt funny. I looked at my hand. I had become animated.

The room began to change. I was in a different place. I saw an orange house. I moved closer. The house was made of carrots! I tried to touch the house. It flew away! I chased the house. It kept flying away.

Finally, a rabbit came out. The rabbit had green fur, and green glasses. The rabbit introduced herself. "I'm Alice," she said.

"I'm Kenna," I said. "May I come in?"

"I'll show you," said Alice. Alice opened the door. The place was a mess.

"Do you have a radio?" I asked.

"Yes," Alice answered.

"We will clean up," I said. After we cleaned up, we went outside and played. Then it got dark. "I'd better go home," I said.

"There is only one way," said Alice. We went through the house.

"Would you come with me?" I asked.

"No, I would just see my backyard," Alice answered.

I went through Alice's door. I looked around. I was back in the cave. I looked at the door. It now said KENNA MEETS ALICE. I knew that if anyone went through the door they would meet Alice. I ran through the cave and behind the trees. I saw my house. I went to my room to write my amazing story in my diary.

Tomorrow I will go back through the orange cave!

Kenna Wallace, Grade 3
Farnsworth Elementary School, Saint Paul
Writer-in-Residence: Stephen Peters

Our Short Adventures

Zaaaappp!

"Ya got 'em!" said Josh.

"Let's go outside," said Jeff.

"Okay. What you want to do?"

"I dunno. Let's explore stuff."

"Okay."

"Hey, let's go over to the old science lab!"

"Sure."

Kreeeeeek, duuuf!

"Oh, now we're locked in!"

Ching! "Ooops!"

"You splashed something on that machine over there!"

"It looks like that thing we saw on the show where the kids go back in time."

"I never saw that thing here before. Let's go in!"

"Okay," said Jeff. Crunch! "Wow! Cool!"

"I wonder what this does?"

"No! Josh! Nooooooo!"

"Wow, I wonder what happened?"

"I don't know, but I'm getting out of this scary machine."

"Me, too."

"Where are we?"

"I don't know. Maybe that thing just shot us into the woods. Okay, when we got in it was pointing west and our house is east, so let's go that way," said Jeff.

"Wow! Look at that tree. I've seen that kind before, but I forgot where. Hummm. Oh, yeah, in my book about uh, no, we got to get out of here fast."

"What's wrong?" said Jeff. "Why are we going back to the machine, Josh. Wait up."

"Hurry up!" said Josh. "You know that tree we saw?"

"Yeah."

"Well, I saw it in my book about dinosaurs!"

"So you're saying. . . . No, it can't be possible!"

"It is, Jeff. Believe it. We went back in time. The tree we saw has been extinct for over sixty million years. We've got to get back home before they find us!"

Rrrrrr!

"What was that?"

"The T. rex!"

Rrrrrr!

"It found us! Hold on! I got an idea. Come here!"

"Got it?"

"Yeah! Here it comes! Come here and eat me! I'm nice and plump!"

"Josh, let it go!"

Thump! Puuf!

"Well, we're stuck here forever unless you can fix this machine. Too bad we had to use the time machine for that. Well, let's go find food."

Andre Palmier, Grade 5
Rossman Elementary School, Detroit Lakes
Writer-in-Residence: Stephen Peters

My Sky

In my pictures I always drew green rolling hills. I had trees with brown trunks and green tops. They were all the same size, and always the same shape. In the middle of my picture was my house. It was always a red square with a brown triangle on the top and a blue window in the middle. On the horizon was my orange sun, a circle with yellow or red streaks coming from it. I always put my sun to the left of my house. Dotting my sky were my black geese. Always the same size and in a M shape. My clouds were white, outlined in blue. My sky was never colored in.

The day after I drew a picture like this, something happened. I was riding my bike with my sister and best friend in the smooth black street. We were all having a good time, laughing and talking. A couple of boys from across the street threw a rock at me and it got caught in my spoke. I remember flipping over my small grey handlebars. I laid there for a moment and then I opened my eyes. Tears immediately rushed down my smooth cheeks. My sister was bending over me, worried. Everything was so confusing. I couldn't talk, I couldn't move. I could hear my best friend crying and the boys laughing. I somehow managed to stand up and stop crying.

Later that night my mom, a skinny woman with curly short blond hair took me to the hospital. The doctor made me put on pink Mickey Mouse pajamas with feet in it. That night I slept in my hard, cold hospital bed with the sounds of beep-beep-beep all around me. I felt so loved that night.

When I sat down to draw a picture after I got back from the hospital, something seemed different. I looked at my picture, exactly the same as all the others, but it wasn't right. My sky seemed so empty.

Lauren Cripe, Grade 9
Oltman Junior High School, Saint Paul Park
Writer-in-Residence: Richard Solly

MY HANDS KNOW SECRETS

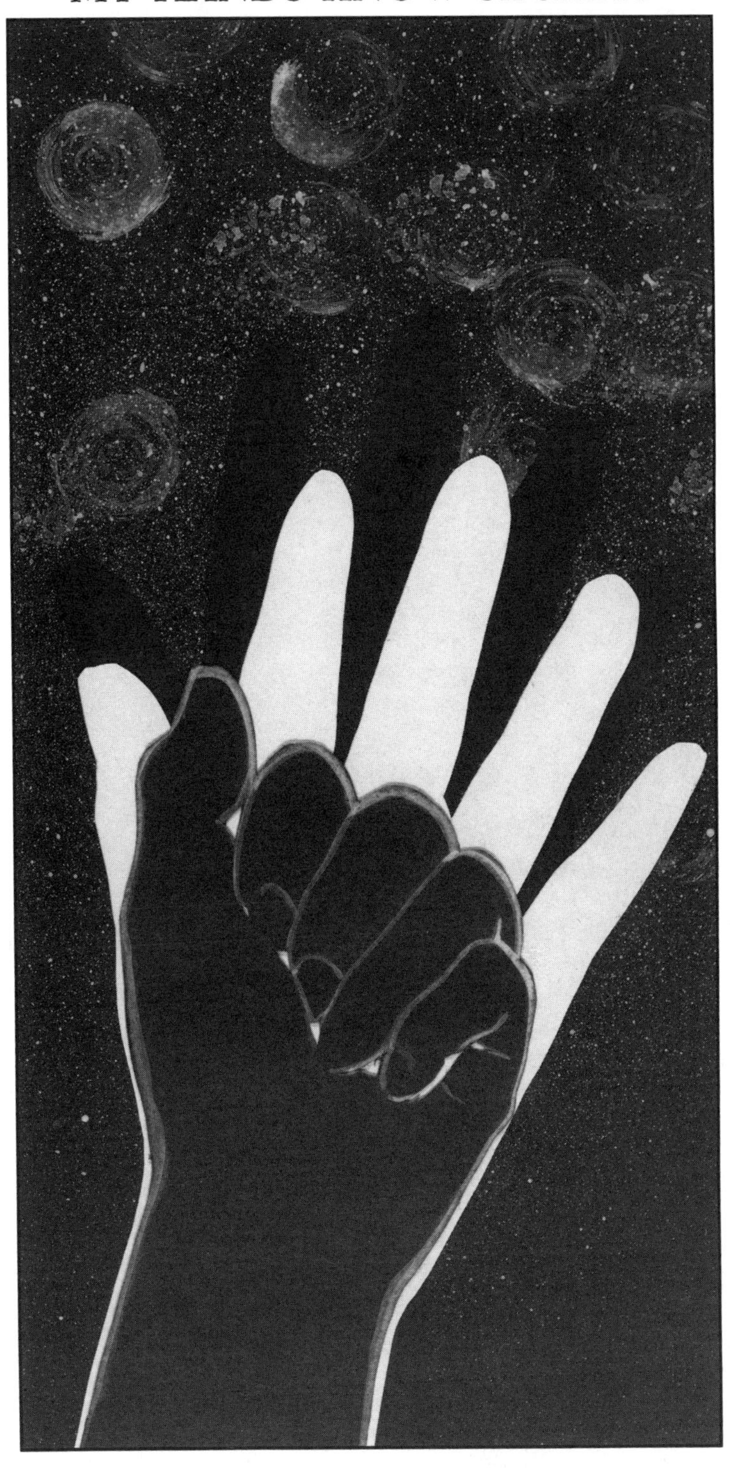

My Hands

My hands know more
than my mind
could ever dream of. . . .

My hands know secrets
never to be spoken.

My hands dream of touching
the sky. . . .
They want to touch
a cave of softness.

My hands smell like grass
newly cut.

My hands look like a canyon
collecting new ideas and dreams
like a river does
to rainwater.

My hands can crackle
like a roaring fire of verses.
They taste like breezes
blowing off the sea.

My hands feel
like the bark of a pine tree.
They hold more ideas
than the mind
can ever imagine.

Leslie Erin Kopatz, Grade 5
Fulton Community School, Minneapolis
Writer-in-Residence: Carol Dines

My Tremendous Trombone

My Trombone
rests in its case
ready to play any minute.
When I open my case
I can almost already hear the music.
My Trombone is like a
cannon ready to shoot at my command.
When I start booming the
noises my cats
run away in fear.
When I stop it feels
like I'm the only person alive.
My cats tremble
when they hear the name
"TROMBONE!"

Dugan Magraw, Grade 5
Chelsea Heights Elementary School, Saint Paul
Writer-in-Residence: Susan Marie Swanson

The White Chalk

The chalk looks like a sleeve
that wiggles when you move your
arm in bed. It is a glass of
milk sitting in the fridge,
on a shelf next to the juice,
waiting for me to drink it with macaroni and cheese.
Its best friend is another piece
of chalk on a high shelf.
It dreams of making a flower on the chalkboard;
it dreams of a heart, a cloud, a puppy.
In my hands it feels soft as mittens lying
on a pillow, soft as fur on a baby tiger.
Sometimes I think it's like ice—
hard and yellow as spray painted ice cubes.
It sounds like a stick rolling down a hill,
running into a tree.
It sounds like a candle being lit with
a blue flame.
And when you are done with the words
the chalk has written, you erase them,
and the world goes black,
waiting for A-B-C's, tigers, a single turtle.
At night you put it away on the shelf.
Tomorrow it will be used again, warmed into words,
this puppet of the hand.

Mrs. Renslo's P.M. Class, Kindergarten
Lake Elmo Elementary School, Lake Elmo
Writer-in-Residence: John Minczeski

The Crack of a Wooden Baseball Bat

We all sit in the dugout waiting to hit. Lenny
steps up to the plate. We're dead.
The pitcher waits for a signal. He pitches a strong
fast ball. Swoosh! Right over the plate.
Strike one. The pitcher waits for another signal.
Another powerhouse fastball. Swoosh! Strike two.
Lenny stands like a statue over the plate. The pitcher
gets cocky. He throws a slow easy pitch. CRACK!!!
Lenny hits it long and hard. He heads for first base.
The center fielder scrambles to catch it. Second base.
The fielder jumps. Third base. And misses. Home. Lenny
wins the game. We drench him with Gatorade. He laughs
and cries at the same time. He is overpowered with emotion.
He can still hear the crack of the wooden baseball bat.

Evan Michael Sieve, Grade 6
Long Prairie Elementary School, Long Prairie
Writer-in-Residence: Diego Vazquez

Mittens

One, two, three, four, five;
I put my hand in-side;
I put my hand inside of my mitten!
Six, seven, eight, nine, ten;
I do it all over again;
I do it over again with my mittens.
My hands have found a home.
My fingers are never alone.
They're always warm when it's cold . . .
in my mittens.

Red, yellow, and green;
I keep them nice and clean;
I keep them nice and clean;
They're my mittens.

Red, yellow, green;
I put them in the washing machine.
I put them in the washing machine.
They're my mittens.

Ms. Johnson's A.M. Class, Kindergarten
Parkway Elementary School, Saint Paul
Musician-in-Residence: Charlie Maguire

My Teeth

This is a poem for my teeth that shine
so brightly. This is a poem for teeth
that have been in my life for a long time.
They fell out and grew back all in a matter
of years, and now keep me company
when I am alone. This is a poem
for my teeth that are not perfect
but are a part of me, always.
They're little white diamonds, sitting,
attached to my gums like gum
on a shoe. Just there. No one will ever know
if they want to be there. This poem is just
for my teeth.

Lauren Zwick, Grade 7
Blake Middle School, Hopkins
Writer-in-Residence: John Minczeski

Hush!

Be quiet, TV, stop talking
loud. I am trying
to sleep.
Refrigerator, refrigerator,
stop creaking. Stop creaking
right now because I am
trying to sleep.
Mom and Dad, stop talking.
I am trying
to sleep. Dream, stop
talking. I am trying
to sleep.
Shadows, stop scaring
me.
I am trying to sleep.
Lightning,
stop scaring me.
Thunder, stop
scaring me.
Wind, stop
swishing.
I am trying to sleep.

Mary Raether, Grade 1
Aquila Primary Center, Saint Louis Park
Writer-in-Residence: Susan Marie Swanson

Takeover

Help, the spirit of Barney has taken over me.
I can feel myself getting fatter.
My face getting longer and I'm getting taller.
Help!
I can feel myself beginning to sing.
Children are all around me, singing
those awful songs that I don't like.
My color has changed.
Now I'm purple and green and I have a tail!
Oh, no, we're beginning a show!

Chee Vang, Grade 6
Parkway Elementary School, Saint Paul
Writer-in-Residence: Roseann Lloyd

On the School Bus

On the school bus
I arrange my stuff
so no one can sit with me.
I leave a spot in the corner open
so I can sit.
I lean my head
against the window.
I stare at the white dirty snow
where uneager students
used to stand,
who have now loaded on the bus.
On the school bus.
I drown out the noises,
those loud noises
that students make
calling to someone
in their seat.
I pay no attention
to anything at all
except the trees
that whisper secrets to one another,
and the way the houses look
with all the snow on top.

Laura Lee, Grade 5
Gatewood Elementary School, Hopkins
Writer-in-Residence: John Minczeski

One Room Schoolhouse

From Minnesota, in a one-room schoolhouse
Ringing the bell, children quiet as a mouse
If you're a woman, you can't be a spouse
Teaching in a one-room schoolhouse

Little Liza, on her way to school
Lunch in her pockets, she was no fool
Dressed so pretty, in her skirt and blouse
Learning in a one-room schoolhouse

–bridge–

Keep the fire going all day long
Singing some grammar in a song
Using a quill for penmanship
Using a slate for arithmetic

From Minnesota, in a one-room schoolhouse
Ringing the bell, children quiet as a mouse
Ringing the bell, school is out
Learning in a one-room schoolhouse

Ms. Eldredge's Class, Grade 5
Linwood A+ Elementary School, Saint Paul
Musician-in-Residence: Charlie Maguire

Advice

Listen to your heart
You might meet your Prince Charming
Don't stick small objects up your nose
Don't run with sharp things
Listen to your friends
You'll need them someday
Remember to cut your nails
Clean behind your ears
Listen to what your parents say
But don't always do what you're told
Rock the boat but don't tip it over
Cover your mouth when you sneeze
Eat your vegetables
Have faith in yourself
Remember the Little Engine that could
Remember to have fun
Everyone wants to be Cinderella once
Always tie your shoes
And don't be scared of the Big Bad Wolf

Denice Olson, Grade 11
KMS High School, Kerkhoven
Writer-in-Residence: Richard Solly

Untitled

Peanut,
like a plump green
pear,
a surge of taste
poked into a salty
morsel small enough
for a termite to tackle.
An addicting taste—when you
run out you feel like
a ball in a pinball machine—
finally settling down
when they run out of
quarters.
The hard shell
is like the bumpy road
to grandma and grandpa's
house. When you finally make
it in, you see two smiling lumps
of gold.

Peter Hannah, Grade 6
Lake Elmo Elementary School, Lake Elmo
Writer-in-Residence: John Minczeski

Cripsy Crab

Down South
Sunny Georgia
I sit in a small ocean side restaurant
Filled with sea creatures and artifacts
My lungs are filled
The delicious aroma of steamy sea food
I order a dozen crisp snow crab legs
I cannot wait for them to arrive
I sip on my ice tea in anticipation
My meal arrives
I take my special tools and crack
open the legs
I discover a nice piece of meat
I dip it into my warm bowl of lemon butter
It feels warm and smooth as I swallow it
Every last piece of meat is finished
and I smile in satisfaction

Melissa Peters, Grade 12
Prior Lake High School, Prior Lake
Writer-in-Residence: Diego Vazquez

Untitled

HELP!
I'm being taken over by video games.
Although a slow process, every time I play
I can feel myself punched and kicked by Sub-Zero
or assisting Michael Jordan with a dunk.
One day, I was completely taken over.
It happened just as Joe Montana
threw the winning touchdown to me.
I was just a little figure
on the screen—I could not
receive anything from the outside world.
I was red, orange, yellow, green, brown, indigo,
and violet. All the colors of the rainbow.
Round, square, rectangle, triangle and people
shapes. I could feel the sweat
running down Roger Clemens' face just before
he pitched the ball to me.
Just before face-off, I felt a jerking
and I
turned
black.

Michael Sullivan, Grade 7
LeSueur-Henderson Secondary School, LeSueur
Writer-in-Residence: Roseann Lloyd

Arizona

I was having a bad day.
Woke up late
Didn't get to eat breakfast.
Made it to work on time.
Then, two hours into the workday the
power went out.
We had to close the store for an hour and a half.
Everybody was armed with a flashlight
as we sat in a circle and thought about
what to do.

It occurred to me,
Why not just leave and go someplace warm
like Arizona.
Just run away from the cold Minnesota
weather and leave everything behind.
To sit by a poolside
soaking up the sun's warm rays
not having to worry about getting
up early to scrape windows
and to warm up your car.
To be able to have nice weather all year round. . . .

My thoughts are interrupted by
bright lights all around me!
The power is back on.
Time to go to work again.

Kara Dinkel, Grade 12
Long Prairie/Grey Eagle High School, Long Prairie
Writer-in-Residence: Diego Vazquez

Silent Listeners

Sometimes I talk to my ears.
I tell them they are like messengers.
They tell me what's going on out
in the giant, exciting world.
I think my ears look like caves
that lead way back where there
might be unexpected treasure.
Treasure that looks like it's from
ancient Egypt. My ears wish that
they could live in a jewelry
store. They love to wear earrings that
have bluebirds with bright, fluffy wings.
My ears work hard, they have huge
muscles. They hold my hair behind them even
when it weighs as much as fourteen
elephants. My ears listen for the
sound of a gun going *bang* before
a race at track and field day.
They listen for the loud booming voice
of my mom shouting "Wake up soon
or you'll miss the bus." Sometimes I
talk to my ears. I wish they
could talk back.

Kelli Billstein, Grade 6
Lake Elmo Elementary School, Lake Elmo
Writer-in-Residence: John Minczeski

Salt

Hi. My name is Lisa Walton. I'd like to tell you one of my favorite stories about myself. It all started when I had to go borrow some salt from my closest neighbor. You see, my neighbor is pretty far away. We live on a mountainside. My neighbor is an old granny. I think she's a witch.

Anyway, I started up the mountain trail on a cool morning. I could see the old shack Granny lived in coming up. It was gray and small and looked like it was around in the Stone Age. "Creak!" went the old steps.

Old Granny opened the door and said, "Well, if it isn't the old Walton girl. How are you?"

"Oh, I'm fine," I said. "I need to borrow some salt."

"Yes, but how do you taste?" said Granny.

"What?" I said.

Granny said, "Never mind, now what did you say you wanted to borrow?"

"Some salt," I said.

"Well, I'll be right back," said Granny.

When she was gone I thought about running or at least hiding, but I stayed right there in my spot. I was getting very bored and started to creep around. I found a window and peered inside. Granny was fumbling around with some sort of a book. She wandered toward my window and I jumped away just in time. "Creak!" the door on the other side of the house was opening. What if she saw me snooping around? My body got tense as the lady called, "Dear, where did you go?" The footsteps stopped and I heard a tin container drop and the lady stepped inside mumbling something about dinner wasted. I walked out to the front of the house and grabbed the tin can. It was full of salt.

"Oh, how nice," I thought. Then I got another thought. What if it was poisoned? I decided to throw it off the side of the mountain. One, two, thr . . . I stopped. I heard footsteps coming near. I ran behind the house.

"Deary, I know you're out there!"

I saw a small trap door and made it inside just before she saw me.

"Wow," I said. The room was so cool, like a laboratory. I walked toward the window and . . . BOOM! I hit a trap door and slid down a slide and out a chute in the wall. I was outside again and this time somewhere different. Oh, I knew the place. It was the other mountain. I saw a bridge and it went to . . . well, I didn't know where.

So I followed it. The bridge was very old and creaked a lot, but I made it across. Uh-oh. There was Granny. She said, "I will eat you now," and she pushed a button and the bridge disappeared. She got an inch away from me and she hit a trap door and ended on the other side of the mountain. I went home.

That story is true and Granny is still living over there at the other side of the mountain. I hope I never have to borrow some more salt again.

Amy Weiby, Grade 4
Grey Cloud Elementary School, Cottage Grove
Writer-in-Residence: Stephen Peters

Inside the World of Movies

Inside the world of movies
Nothing is the same
Different companies, different actors, different directors
It could be a movie of love and romance
Or a movie of murder and terror
It could be Romeo and Juliet gracing the screen
Or Mickey and Mallory Knox slaughtering some unknown victim
There could be friendly aliens as E.T.
Or a vicious creature ripping out someone's heart
There could even be a nice scenic drive to Mexico
Or a bar in Mexico filled with vampires
And there is a myth that through all the hard work
Money and fame will bring eternal happiness and a new movie.

John Weber, Grade 9
Worthington Junior High School, Worthington
Writer-in-Residence: Richard Solly

Sounds of My Bus Driver

I hear her say, "Book bags out of the aisle."
I hear the voice of others mumbling disgust.

I hear the bus driver threatening,
"I'll get Ms. Rowe."
Then I hear the kids go, "Oooooooo"

I hear her read the safety manual to us,
"no eating, drinking, standing, walking, yelling on the bus."
I hear everyone laughing, knowing it will never happen.

I hear her say, "no broken pencils. If there are any,
I know they're from St. Joe's."
I also hear a younger student snapping pencils.

Then I hear myself as I get off, say,
"Bye, Mrs. Bus Driver."
And hear her reply, "Yeah, yeah, yeah."

I really think she likes us!

Joe Campbell, Grade 8
Saint Joseph's School, West Saint Paul
Writer-in-Residence: Sigrid Bergie

LURKING IN THOSE SHADOWS

Guilt

Why are you there,
lurking in those shadows,
stalking my consciousness?
Loosen your grip,
allow me to escape your venom.
You are there, but for what?
Can't I shed your distasteful
feathers
and let them drop down, down
to the waters below?
Though I forbid you to enter,
you sneak in unmercifully
until all my thoughts
are focused on you.
Stop! Stop! Let me be.
But no, you return, your constant
pulses throb in my head
like a headache, a huge headache
that robs me of happiness.
What is the reason? What have I done?

Katie Vang, Grade 7
Blake Middle School, Hopkins
Writer-in-Residence: John Minczeski

Adopted

adopted, a sad whale looking for a home in the
  water alone . . .
adopted, mix of color and questions . . . adopted
  a happy hope waiting for someone to come
  and take you in the love boat of freedom
adopted, worry floating in a bottle . . .
and then dying—dying into emptiness
adopted, too many puzzle pieces scrambled
flying to an eagle's wing and floating into the
mind of me . . . me.
adopted, a bird that can't fly to its mother—
its mother
adopted, when—why—how?
adopted, I want to be with you my God, my mother.
adopted, a happiness and sadness, too much
Getting a chance to love someone you've never met.
    Adopted.

Emily Mader, Grade 4
Katherine Curren Elementary School, Hopkins
Writer-in-Residence: Sheila O'Connor

Hurt

It began with a sad song
broke into a war
words of madness came
from people around me
hatred causing death
loss of friends and family
people separated from
the world, gun shots, knife
fights, and the music went on.

Lora Pipenhagen, Grade 10
Swanville Public School, Swanville
Writer-in-Residence: Diego Vazquez

Escape to America

Natasha was packing to leave when the door bell rang. She went to answer it and through the window she saw two soldiers. She was scared. She opened the door and one said, "Ma'm, people are saying you are planning to go to America, is this true?"

"Yes, I am going to America," Natasha answered.

"We are sorry you cannot leave, the war has started," was his reply. "You will have to come with us."

Natasha's heart sank as she was thinking, how am I going to get to America. "In that case I will not go to America," she said sadly.

"If this is true our job here is done," was the soldier's reply. But he warned, "Don't get any ideas about slipping away, we'll be watching you."

By this time Natasha felt hopeless. How could she possibly sneak onto the train with the soldiers watching her. She started to reconsider her trip, but knew in her heart if she stayed she would die for sure. So she finished packing and left.

She found a spot on the train in a boxcar and settled in. She looked through a crack in the wall and saw a soldier checking the boxcars for stowaways. He was heading straight for the car she was in when there was a terrible scream. The soldier turned and walked toward the scream and the train started moving.

The next morning the train stopped at a station and Natasha overheard the conductor talking to a soldier. He wanted to check for stowaways because they had heard screams at the last station. Natasha was scared and needed to find a place to hide. All there was in the boxcar was some hay and boxes. She tried to get in one of them, but she didn't fit. So she tried another one and she almost fit, but not quite. She was trying to find another spot when the door started to open. Looking into the boxcar was the soldier. Suddenly another man appeared and told the soldier there was a phone call for him in the station. The solder took one last glance and walked back to the station. Then the man looked right at Natasha and began to close the door without saying a word.

Natasha said in a soft voice, "Thank you."

"I hope you have a safe trip," he said just as softly. The door went shut just as the train started to move.

Natasha knew that the next stop would bring her close to her boat. She planned to get off the train immediately and make her way to the boat.

As Natasha walked up the plank she wondered if the soldiers would be waiting. She could barely believe it when her ticket was accepted without any question.

It took 13 days to get to America. When Natasha arrived she found a place to live and began her new life.

Shannon von Helmst, Grade 4
Willow River Elementary School, Hudson, Wisconsin
Writer-in-Residence: Stephen Peters

The Gift of a Smile

I see you sitting there and you do
not smile. I see you walking
and you do not smile. I see you
talking and still you do not smile.

So I will give you my smile. My smile
may be ugly, but at least it's there. Happy
bright, and energetic, you will never want
it to leave. You will be happy once again.

I will see you sitting and you will finally
be smiling. I will see you walking and you
will be smiling. And I will see you talking
and you will be smiling.

Shaama Saber, Grade 9
Dassel-Cokato High School, Cokato
Writer-in-Residence: Diego Vazquez

Untitled

I never knew I loved
smushed potato chips on my PB and Js.
I never knew I loved
anatomy or water
until I heard *Aqualung*
which has nothing to do with
anatomy or water.
I never knew I loved my life until I thought
about missing my
sandwiches and *Aqualung*.
I never knew I loved
anything until I
had a passionate hatred for it all.
I never knew I loved fishing
until my line froze in the eye
and I put it in my mouth to thaw it
and froze my lips instead.
I never knew I loved books
until I quit reading them.
I never knew I loved my pets
until puppy breathed his bad breath
and kitty killed mousey.
I never knew I loved January
until mousey was killed,
buried in the frozen ground
and I saw a swan fly overhead.
I never thought I knew much
until I wrote it all down.
I never knew I loved me
until I stopped to look at myself.

Meghann Ovre, Grade 12
Stillwater High School, Stillwater
Writer-in-Residence; John Minczeski

The Mystery

"Leave me alone!" Kisha yelled as she turned around at Juwan, who was walking behind her from after school until five p.m. She had been annoyed all day by Juwan asking all these silly questions. Her face started to turn red and looked like she was about to blow up. "I wish you would go find someone else to bother instead of me!" Kisha yelled.

Just as Juwan was about to speak up, Kisha started yelling again. "You are very annoying! Go away and leave me alone! Go!" She pointed her finger toward the other direction. Stomping her feet as hard as she could, she turned around and started walking again.

Kisha and Juwan are in the same fifth grade class. Kisha has a little brother who's in third grade. He followed Kisha and started copying her, stomping his feet. Kisha was so annoyed, so she gave up. "Okay, you can come with me, but no more questions about that spooky mountain of yours, who or wherever you heard it from."

"You got my word," he said happily.

Then they went to get some slushy from a store they had never seen before. Kisha thought they just opened or something.

When they got out, they started down to the corner and saw misty fogs. Then, suddenly an old woman popped right in front of them. She was as tall as Kisha and Juwan. She had yellow rotten teeth, and was skinny as a toothpick. "Wh-wh-what do you want?" they both asked at the same time.

"Oh, nothing much, but this is for you two. Here, take it," she said as she shoved it to Kisha's hand. She then walked down the street and disappeared into the fog.

"I swear I've never seen her around before," Kisha told Juwan.

"Me either," he told her. They ran as fast as they could to Kisha's apartment, fifth floor, number 514. Juwan lived next door, room 515. They went inside and quickly locked all the doors. Gasping for breath, they sat down at the kitchen table. Kisha suddenly remembered the thing that woman gave her. She opened it and read, "The Mystery of the Spooky Mountain."

Juwan's eyes suddenly opened wide and he snatched the book from her. "Wow," he said when he saw it. "It is real. I told you it was real, but did you believe me? No . . ."

"Oh whatever," she said. "It's just a story. How can you actually believe it?"

"You never believe anything," he mumbled.

"What did you say?" she asked.

"Nothing," he answered back. "Let's just read the book," he told her.

They opened the book and read the warning: "If you must read this, you shall finish it or if you don't, don't fall asleep."

"Okay what's that supposed to mean?" she asked. They started chapter one, "The Unknown Road." They finished chapter one, and Kisha wanted to stop. Juwan told her that they shouldn't but Kisha said, "The book was in my hand, so I'm in charge of it."

"But . . . but . . . the warning said . . . "

Just as Juwan was about to finish his sentence, Kisha interrupted and said, "Oh come on, quit being a baby."

"I'm not being a baby," he yelled. He headed for the door, turned around, stuck out his tongue, and then slammed the door behind him. Kisha ignored him and put the book on the table. She cleaned up and was very tired. She told Juan, her brother, to call her up when their parents got home. Juwan sat in his apartment and thought of what happened, the weird store, and that little woman.

He quickly went back to the street where the store was. He walked down there, but then didn't see the store. He ran back to Kisha's apartment, forgetting that he was still mad at her. He knocked and Juan answered the door. "Hey there Juan, where's your sister?"

"Right there on the couch, sleep'n'," Juan said.

"What? She didn't follow the directions?" Juwan yelled.

"What are you talking about? I just don't get ya," Juan said.

Juwan rushed in and tried to wake Kisha up. "Kisha, Kisha, wake up!" he yelled.

"Where is this place?" Kisha asked. Just then she heard Juwan calling her. She tried answering back but it seemed like he couldn't hear her. "Juwan! I'm right here, can you hear me?" she yelled, but still Juwan kept calling for her.

"Quick, I've got to find a way to sleep too!" he told Juan. Then he handed him the book and told Juan to give it to his parents when they get home. Juan was very confused by that time, but he helped Juwan fall asleep.

Then Juwan finally fell asleep. Where am I? he asked himself. He then spotted Kisha and ran to her.

"Oh! I'm so glad to see you here." She hugged him when she saw him. Juwan explained about the store and the little woman to Kisha. "Oh I'm so sorry. I should have listened to you," she cried. "We're stuck here forever."

"Not exactly," he told her. "We still have a chance, if your parents would just finish the story then we might have a chance to get out of here."

"I hope they will," Kisha said in an unconfident voice.

Three hours later, the door opened and Mr. and Mrs. Eldola were home. "Mama, Papa!" yelled Juan. "Kisha and Juwan's sleeping, I try waking them up but they won't. Oh and they told me to give this to you."

"What's this for?" they asked.

"I don't know, they told me to give to you, so I give it to you," Juan said.

"You've got to learn how to talk right, Juan."

He gave them a brief smile.

Mr. Eldola wanted to call the cops but Mrs. Eldola said not to. They opened the book and started to read. "Hey Kisha and Juwan are in here," they said.

As they continued the story, Kisha and Juwan heard them reading.

"Oh no! They're reading the story, too," Kisha yelled.

"Be patient, Kisha. As long as they don't fall asleep, they'll be fine," Juwan told her.

"But what if they do fall asleep?" she said as she started to cry. "We're trapped! We'll never get out of here!"

"We'll get out of here. Just stay calm," he said.

Mr. and Mrs. Eldola read until Chapter 7. "Three more chapters to go," Juan said. "You can do it, Mom and Dad. Just three more chapters." They tried to keep their eyes open, but it was too much and their eyes started to close.

"Where are we now?" Mr. Eldola asked his wife. They walked for awhile and spotted their daughter and Juwan.

"Mom, Dad!" "Mr. and Mrs. Eldola!" they yelled.

"What is going on?" Mr. and Mrs. Eldola asked them. So they told them what happened.

"So the only way out is if Juan finishes the story now?"

"I believe that's the only way," Juwan answered.

They all counted on Juan, who was only eight years old. Three more chapters until the book was finished. Juan took the book. "Cool," he said. Then he started reading. He was on the last chapter when his eyes started to close. He started to fall into the world of trapness where you can never get out. Just then the clock struck twelve. That woke him up. He continued the book.

Juwan, Kisha, Mr. and Mrs. Eldola continued their walk. They found an old hut. They saw the light and weren't sure if they should go in. They went in and what they saw was a weird thing. On the table was a note for them.

"It's like they expected us to drop by," Mr. Eldola said.

The note said, "To Whom It May Concern, The Spooky Mountain is not scary. It has disappeared thousands of years ago. It disappeared for so long that it became a legend so people never think that it's real."

Just as they had finished, they heard Juan calling them and they woke up.

After what had happened they were sure to burn the book. Juan thought it was really cool. He kept yapping about it but it was already enough for Juwan.

"Well it's time for me to go. My parents will be home any minute now."

"Wait!" Kisha yelled as he opened the door. "I want to say I'm sorry. Friends?"

"Friends," he said as he gave her a wink and left.

Yen Dang, Grade 6
Parkway Elementary School, Saint Paul
Writer-in-Residence: Stephen Peters

The Scary Room

My teacher looking like a teddy all curled up,
Reading very soft like a cloud. The little
girl making tipis, but they look like horns or
party hats. The head of the girl has
water in a balloon that an arrow
is pointing at. Robot's head looking
at the soft book. Why is my teacher
reading the book making me draw these
scared sunny drawings? Having a rubber
seat that makes me blubber is this what's
in my classroom? Having a bean as a cup.
My teacher's head like a bubble, the room
like a scary monster. The janitor
sweeping up my cries.

Megan Skogmo, Grade 6
Lincoln Elementary School, Detroit Lakes
Writer-in-Residence: Margot Fortunato Galt

The Stand-Off

"Do it, Tommy I dare you!" said Bruce.

"No, not alone Bruce!" said Tommy with his knees shaking.

"Fine then, baby, we'll all go with you!" Bruce declared loudly.

Tommy stood on the sidewalk, just looking at the house. He stuttered to find an excuse not to go but nothing would convince Bruce.

Unwillingly, the crowd struggled through overgrown grass and under a broken trellis up to the house. It was grey with broken windows, bricks missing from the chimney and the front door, what was left of it, hung open.

Tommy peeked through the door and said with a quivery voice, "Anyone home?" Only echoes answered him.

"Well, baby, whatcha waiting for? Lead the way!" Bruce slyly demanded.

Tommy cautiously made his way in. The floor cracked as the group shuffled in. They all coughed from the dust and the musty smell. To the left was a staircase with about six missing steps and to the right a living room all perfectly arranged with sheet-covered furniture and plastic over the lamps. They had one of two choices and Tommy had to make it.

He started for the staircase but then suddenly turned towards the living room. Bruce followed his every move cautiously. Everyone was breathing hard and gazing at the house.

Suddenly Bruce jumped, "Ahh!"

"What?" Tommy asked.

"I saw something!" claimed Bruce regaining his breath. "Over there, behind the curtains!" he whispered.

All at once, everyone looked over at the drapes.

"Someone has to look!" Bruce said. "Tommy, you go, now!" Bruce exclaimed.

"I can't go, um, I, I, I have to . . . go home for lunch. My mommy is calling me!" Tommy pleaded.

"Go now or you lose the bet!"

"Fine but I don't want a white casket for the funeral!"

Slowly he crept toward the damp curtains and managed to gain the strength to move the dusty drapery. Suddenly a bat flew from the top of the curtains. Everybody started screaming. It was crazy. Girls running around pointlessly, guys jumping, everyone frantically searching for the door.

Then Tommy screamed above everyone, "Gotcha!" and ran home as fast as his little legs could carry him.

Bruce screamed down the street, "I'll get you Tommy Stergin, you'll see. I'll get you!"

Dana Hegre, Grade 8
Meyer Middle School, River Falls, Wisconsin
Writer-in-Residence: Stephen Peters

The Menard's Man

I am scared of that Menard's man
who pops up on the TV every hour or
so.

He somehow gets into my TV and starts
shouting at me about bronze door hinges
and house siding
with his big black glasses,
elastic mouth, and blue sweater.

I want to change the channel but my dad
says, "No, I want to watch *Star Trek.*"
So I have to sit through the whole 30 seconds
of the commercial!

Sarah Fuller, Grade 6
Pullman Elementary School, Saint Paul Park
Writer-in-Residence; Diego Vazquez

Stella and Martha

Once upon a time there was a little girl who lived in a country far away. The girl was eight years old with blond hair and green eyes. Her name was Stella. She lived with her father who was very lonely because his wife died several years before. The little girl was very sad too because all of her friends had mothers who would make dinner, clean the house and wash clothes. All the things Stella and her dad had to do.

All of the time Stella would sit in her secret place down by the big lake watching the ducks paddle around thinking what it would be like to have a mother to help around the house. The secret place had trees and bushes all around a grassy meadow. Stella could sit down and no one could see her. One day when she was watching the ducks, she fell asleep and had a weird dream. Stella dreamt that one of the ducks, a big green mallard, could talk. The duck told Stella that she had a mother. The mother had blond hair and green eyes like Stella. Her mother did help with all of the work Stella and her father had to do but there was something more. She could not think what was missing.

Stella woke up and it was dark and cold. She ran home to tell her father about the dream. Her dad was not home. She could not remember what the mother in the dream said to her. She did not know where her dad was. She was very scared and started to cry. Her dad came home and said, "I'm sorry that I did not come home." Stella told him about her weird dream. Her dad was surprised because that very day he had met a woman with green eyes and blond hair. He promised to see her again and introduce Stella to her.

Stella went with her dad to meet the lady. The lady was very tall and pretty. Her name was Martha. She liked her very much. So did her dad who told Stella that he would marry her. She would be Stella's new mother.

After living with Martha for many months Stella finally remembered what the duck had tried to tell her. A mother is much more than someone to do all the work. Martha became Stella's best friend and both she and her dad were very happy. No longer did she go by the big lake. She was having too much fun with Martha.

Annie Russell, Grade 4
Saint Joseph's School, West Saint Paul
Writer-in-Residence: John Coy

You and Me

(Lisa on flute)

refrain

You and me, (you and me)
We've been together so long
You and me, (you and me)
Since we sang our first song. . . .
We are just the last class, and we're here to say
Just a few memories before we go away
(Before we go away) . . .

verse

A, B, C, (A, B, C,)
That's how it all began
For you and me, (you and me)
At the "Read-In" dancing to the band
Remember the tree-house in Kindergarten
And the doctor bag
Every morning we pledge allegiance to the flag

Now is the time, to say goodbye
All of our memories will never die

You and me (you and me)
We've been together so long
You and me (you and me)
Since we sang our first song

We are the last class, and we're here to say
So long Elmore Elementary, we're going away
So long Elmore Elementary, we're going away
So long Elmore Elementary, we're going away

(Kelly on harmonica)

Miss Johnson's Class, Grade 5 and 6
Elmore Elementary School, Elmore
Musician-in-Residence: Charlie Maguire

Ode to Silence

Silence isn't the dog
howling at the moonlight
nor the jets soaring
in the sky. Silence is the blinking
of an eye. Silence is a hand opening.
Silence is the lonely turtle lying
on a rock in the middle of the
beach. Silence is the snowflakes
resting peacefully on the ground. Silence is
the pond as calm as a turned off t.v.
Silence is the pencil writing
in a notebook. Silence is the
breathing of your baby brother
dreaming in his crib. Silence is the
skeleton napping in the grave.

Willie Knaeble, Grade 4
Meadowbrook Elementary School, Hopkins
Writer-in-Residence: Dana Jensen

DREAM THE DREAMS YOU HAVEN'T DREAMED

Just My Theory

each of us has a special stretch of sky
and every hope and dream we have
appears as a shining star
in our special stretch of sky
our strong longing, impossible dreams
become as bright as a bonfire's glow
your dreams that come and die and
come again flicker in the moonlight
and all the dreams you haven't
dreamed are the darkness—so everyone
go to sleep and dream the
dreams we haven't dreamed.

Laura Martell, Grade 5
Glen Lake Elementary School, Hopkins
Writer-in-Residence: Dana Jensen

Patchwork Perspectives

Dreams—autumn leaves,
pools of thoughts, like an abyss of emulsions
flinging, floating, fleeting,
seemingly patternless.
Autumn leaves—do you have a mind of your own?
Or only a creator's whim.
Sun-faded green, then rustic red,
splashes of orange and yellow,
my grandma's patchwork quilt.

Dreams—autumn leaves
delicate as soft, off-white dandelion fuzz,
a lone hill on the Great Plains.
Autumn leaves—fragile to the cheapest
    plastic handle and plastic prongs,
society this, and society that.
Gnarled, blackened wart, spring's first precious daffodil.
Deceiving, two-way mirror.
Dreams—autumn leaves.

Ginny Sawyer, Grade 10
Battle Lake Secondary School, Battle Lake
Writer-in-Residence: John Minczeski

Dreams & Hope

Dreams are hope
I said to the moon
And the moon said
I would like to have a rope
so people can climb and see
All that there is to me.
I want them to understand
that I am just like earth land
but nope
no one will visit me
that's why I don't like to hope.

Amanda Burow, Grade 4
La Crescent Elementary School, La Crescent
Writer-in-Residence: Jovelyn Richards

Untitled

I want to get out of here.
Dreams like a candle.
The way to blow out.
There they go—they're just gone.
A way to get away from the traffic,
traffic like people waiting to move on.
It was a dream,
the sister act we play.
I want to go down
all the way—
a trigger in the gun
we aim.
It's the way we play,
our new generation's way.
Don't aim for me.

Pam Paulson, Grade 11
Roseau High School, Roseau
Writer-in-Residence: John Minczeski

Infinity

Infinity
is not about space or stars
infinity is about colors of worms that are flying in the sky.
Infinity becomes part of everyone
who went to Woodstock
Everything infinity is
is everything it's not.
Simple words like *Buenos noches* cannot tell
the complexity of infinity
Infinity is the confines of the mind
the buzzing of the lights at school
is infinity
yet, they are not
nothing is
infinity
infinity is the color clear
like my cat
the heart's only beat becomes
infinity
which in turn fades out
the Nile in Egypt is sometimes
infinity
is a candle burning in the night
like on Chanukah
the candle blinds infinity
infinity can never be blinded
never be stopped
infinity is a folder that yearns to be
opened up

infinity is a water tower
with an elephant sitting
on it
infinity is
His eyes

Mary Thrall, Grade 7
Central Middle School, Columbia Heights
Writer-in-Residence: Richard Solly

What's Your Dream?

refrain

What's your dream?
What do you want to do?
What's your dream
What do you want to do?
What's your dream?
I've got big dreams too

I want to be a singer on the stage
A story-writer that turns the page
A baseball player hitting a home run
A saxophone player just for fun

I want to be a bus driver, "Good Morning To You!"
Want to play the piano, is what I want to do
I want to be an artist that draws and paints
I want to play football for the New Orleans Saints

I want to be a dancer that rocks and rolls
I want to be a soccer player that kicks those goals
I want to be a doctor when I grow up
Want to be a hockey player that hits the puck.

Ms. Killian's Class, Grade 4
Parkway Elementary School, Saint Paul
Musician-in-Residence: Charlie Maguire

The Clever Man

Once upon a time there lived a young man. His name was Xue Xiong. He was poor, and weak, but he was really, really clever. All he wanted was to have power and to be a lot smarter. One day he went to the King of China. Xue asked, "Can you give me wisdom and power?" The King said, "Only if you get me some gold under the ground." Xue said, "Okay." So Xue went home. He dug and dug and kept on digging. He never stopped digging until he hit something. He dug the thing out. There was a key with the thing he hit. He opened the box. It was the goldest gold. He closed the key when he opened the box and then he closed the box and took it to the King of China. When the King opened it, he was the richest man ever. And the King gave Xue the power and wisdom. Now Xue was the cleverest and smartest boy in China and then Xue was very, very happy.

Xue Xiong, Grade 3
Parkway Elementary School, Saint Paul
Writer-in-Residence: Stephen Peters

The Quest

One day I was strolling through the forest in which I lived when the King and Queen of Tropica called me before them and told me this: "Molly, you must go over the mountains and you will find something that will lead you to my treasure and hurry, you don't have much time." I ran back to my room and packed all my things into a large pack that I would carry with me on my quest.

I started to walk toward the mountains that were lumbering over me like giants. When I finally reached the top I was soaking wet from the sweat. I limped to a forest surrounded by trees letting only in a little bit of light. Suddenly a cold gust of wind came upon me and sent chills down my spine. I was about to leave when I smelled a fragrance indescribable. I turned around and to my amazement there was a unicorn standing in the light and I knew she would lead me to where I was supposed to go. The unicorn gracefully started to run. I ran with all my might to catch her. I could hear her hooves beating against the rough ground. Then suddenly the noise was gone. I looked up and saw why. I was falling off a cliff! Was I going to get the treasure after all? When I hit the water, I tasted the salty water and was gasping for air. When I finally came ashore my clothes were wet and dripped from the water thrashing me around. I lay there not knowing what to do. I smelled the fragrant smell that I had smelled when I was in the forest.

When I finally opened my eyes the unicorn was above me, but this unicorn was smaller. I quickly got up and looked for the other unicorn. She was standing by a large sparkling waterfall. I could hear the water splashing against the rocks beneath. The little unicorn nudged me lightly and started to gallop toward the waterfall. I followed behind them. I walked under the waterfall.

Then suddenly a large dragon jumped out at me and started hissing at me. I was so frightened I stood there with my mouth wide open waiting to scream, but nothing came out. At that time I knew what I had to do. I reached into my pocket and pulled out a piece of soggy bread from my wet pack. I was shaking so hard I could hardly throw it to the dragon, but I managed to lightly toss the bread. When the dragon opened his mouth I could smell a familiar smell, but I couldn't figure it out. Once the dragon got the bread he angrily demanded more. I looked back at the unicorns but they were gone.

The dragon picked me up and started to fly away. "The treasure," I stammered. Crunched into the dragon's palm I wondered if I'd ever get the treasure or even see the King and Queen. I wondered if I'd ever see my room with the pink and purple curtains, my comfortable bed and my . . . Suddenly I was upside-down. What was the dragon going to do to me? Thinking about it I struggled to kick the palm of the dragon's hand, but it was no use; I was too small.

Then I thought about what to do. Well everyone has some weakness, what's mine? I'm ticklish! I grabbed a feather from within my bag and started tickling the dragon's palm, gradually the dragon's palm opened. When it was almost open I realized we were still in the air. I most certainly couldn't jump. I'd have to wait till we got closer to the ground. After awhile the inside of the dragon's palm was sweaty and I had a lack of oxygen, his fist was so tight. Suddenly we hit the ground.

To my surprise his hand opened and I could see the King and Queen. I was back in Tropica. The Queen was so happy, "You did it," the Queen said.

"What did I do, I didn't do anything? I didn't even get your treasure."

The King and Queen explained to me how the dragon was their treasure. "Molly," they said, "this dragon is our son, a spell was cast upon him and only you could free him, we knew we could trust you to do as you were told." Then the King and Queen went on to say "To thank you we would like you to become our Princess." Now I was not only Molly, but Princess Molly!

Molly Umbreit, Grade 5
Grey Cloud Elementary School, Cottage Grove
Writer-in-Residence: Stephen Peters

Letter to Cinderella

Cinderella, Cinderella, wash the floor,
Clean the laundry.
I am your step-mother,
I am reality.
Stop living a fairy-tale.
And start living,
Living for me and your step-sisters,
Living for us,
Cleaning for us,
Cooking for us.
That is the life you shall have.

In your fairy-tale,
You had the glass slipper,
You had the carriage,
And you had the prince.
But this is not a fairy tale,
This is the real world,
And in the real world you
Don't get a glass slipper
And a carriage.
In the real world you get me,
Your stop-mother,
Your reality.

Callie Myers, Grade 8
Central Middle School, Columbia Heights
Writer-in-Residence: Richard Solly

The Story of J.P.

Once upon a time there was a man named J.P. J.P. was as big as a baseball card. He lived in a baseball card store in Milwaukee, in an abandoned mouse hole behind a desk. He slept on a baseball card bed. His pillow was made of cut up baseball cards. His job was to pick up pennies and things. One day the store closed, and J.P. had to find a new home.

He found a home in a used car store. He found an abandoned mouse hole behind the desk. A boy forgot his toy car at the used car store.

J.P. got in and turned the key and drove to the park. He found a tree that had a hole in the bottom and parked his car. He found some leaves for his bed. He also found some leather for his pillow.

He lived in the hole for 2 months. Then the tree died. He got in his car and drove to Illinois.

He found a baseball card store and found an abandoned mouse hole behind the desk. He found some baseball cards and made a bed. His pillow is made of a Ty Cobb baseball card.

Nat Chowen, Grade 3
Chelsea Heights Elementary School, Saint Paul
Writer-in-Residence: Susan Marie Swanson

The First Volcano

Hi, my name is Drelb, and I live in a small village in the woods. I am a halfling, a race of short people. I live in a burrow in the side of a hill. I am going to tell you about my adventure. But f— "Drelb, don't forget that pail of water." "Yes, dear." Sorry for that interruption, that was my wife. Now before I tell you about my adventure, I will tell you a little about me and where I live. I am about 3 and a half feet tall, I have dark brown hair, and I don't wear shoes because they are uncomfortable. We live next to my friend, Lars. He is a few years younger than me. He came along with me on my adventure. Now I will sit down and get cozy in front of the fire and tell you all about my story. It all started when an evil dragon named Volcan started attacking our town. He burned our crops and wounded some of our best warriors. It was a large green dragon with slimy green scales, and long black wings. He had dark blue eyes and yellow stained teeth. He breathed fire that scorched living trees black. We finally said that this dragon needs to be taken care of soon or our whole village would be destroyed. We sat around a table in my house, and started our long, tedious planning. We knew where the dragon's lair was. It was in the heart of the forest where the large mountains were. We knew the fastest way to go was to have the Golden Eagles fly us. We asked around the town if anyone would volunteer to come. After persuading and begging we got three more people to come. Our group consisted of me, Lars, Carok, Martin, and the oldest halfling known, Ganludator. He was the only wizard known that lived in the forest. He said he would pay for the supplies for our expedition. The armorer rummaged up some leather armor, shields, and some finely crafted helmets. The weaponsmith got some short swords and sold them to us. We bought some supplies and packed up that day. We were to meet the eagles two miles into the forest. There they would take us to the river. We then would walk along the river's edge until we got to the dragon's lair. The forest was bright and peaceful. The birds were chirping and we made it there a short while after. There were three eagles to take us. Ganludator rode on the biggest one for he was the largest of the bunch. I rode with Lars and Carok and Martin rode on the last eagle. They glided swiftly through the air. Ganludator said that we will be there shortly. We landed there a few minutes after he said that. I had never been this far into the forest before. The river was gorgeous. The water was clear and blue like the sky. The trees were the greenest I ever saw. We said good-bye to the eagles and thanked them ever so kindly. They were off in a flash. We then started our journey to the dragon's lair. It seemed like it kept moving away from us. At nightfall we set up camp. It was a clear sky with a full moon. I soon fell asleep. When I awoke in the morning the others were already up. We ate a quick breakfast and set off. We stopped only two more times that day. At night we all gathered around the fire and talked about what would happen the next morning. We decided that we would try to catch the dragon by surprise. Ganludator had studied some books on dragons before we left. He said that it should have some kind of weak spot somewhere on its body. If we could strike there it would die. He said that we should try to trick it into showing us where it is by making him unaware of what we're doing. Then we all went to sleep. We all awakened early that morning. It was still dark when we left. A few minutes later we came to the mouth of the cave. We heard some rumbling. We entered and I saw that he was sleeping. All of a sudden Martin let out a great cry and leapt at the dragon. I started to yell no, but it was too late. The dragon awoke and blew a jet of blue flames at him. It got up and said "What do we have here?" Then he ran at us. He got to the mouth of the cave and ran out. Then as we planned we attacked and searched for the weak spot. I went for a rear attack and saw a spot where there were no scales. I jumped up as high as I could. I landed a foot away from it. I yanked out my sword and drove it in as deep as I could. All of a sudden a shrill scream filled the air, and right beneath me the dragon turned to stone. We then knew that was the last of the dragon. We traveled home and as we neared the village, the people started a welcome home parade. The food at the festival was delicious. That night before I went to sleep I looked out my window and saw the dragon turned to stone and fire and a liquid like fire came out so we called it a volcano after the evil green dragon. That was the last we saw of dragons in this part of the woods.

Eric Norton, Grade 7
Rushford-Peterson Middle School, Rushford
Writer-in-Residence: Stephen Peters

The Story of the Sword

Inside the world of the sword
tempers are high,
being stuck in red hot coals
then pounded with a hammer
like we did something wrong.
After that we are either sold
or given away.
Once in someone's possession
we're calm and docile one minute
while the next we are spilling blood
everywhere we go.
There is a myth that William Wallace's sword,
the sword that I am a part of,
was taken by the King of England
and kept over time
then in 1904 it was melted down
and shaped into the Titanic's hull
to curse her maiden voyage.

Rob Young, Grade 9
Northfield High School, Northfield
Writer-in-Residence: Richard Solly

Santa's Universal Adventure

Once upon a time there lived a jolly old elf who, every Christmas Eve, traveled the universe in a magic sleigh led by eight magical reindeer. Together, they were able to deliver toys across the universe in one night. This particular old elf was not only known by the people of Earth, but was known and familiar to all of the beings of the universe, most of whom were even stranger than us. He handed out toys to young Wocks, Sooks and Whoos, and even the cuckoo Babana Fruts from the Planet Nudroz. From nation to state, from planet to home, as he zoomed through the air, the things within the bag began to disappear, one by one.

It seemed, unfortunately, that every year he'd run into some resistance. It usually occurred between Jupiter and Saturn. To the more updated people, this place was called the land of the Koos. These aliens were known to be the most evil aliens in the entire galaxy, not to mention the worst smelling. Every year they had a new plan to destroy Christmas and Santa. But usually the Koos didn't have very smart plans to capture this plump old elf.

This year, it was a whole new ball game. One of the head Christmas destruction designers, named Ababaka Smuthipoo, had recently stumbled upon a new technology that they were sure would be quite sufficient to capture Santa. It was supposed to be able to warp Santa straight to the dungeon when he crossed the border between Jupiter and Uranus, which was right between Jupiter and Saturn. But while all this evil plotting was going on in the land of the Koos, the Elves had just designed a brand new sled for Santa, which in a test run was clocked at light speed. The reindeer liked the idea too, surprisingly, considering the fact that many of them had just had children. It had everything Santa would need and one hundred times more. It had a transporter so Santa didn't have to carry all the toys but instead had them transported straight to his sled when he arrived at a house. It also had a device that could locate Santa if he was in any kind of accident.

It was Christmas Eve. Last minute adjustments were going on all over at Santa's workshop. Santa continued bundling up for the cold winter's night. When all was prepared, the reindeer wished him luck and then he was off, into the night like a marble in the cold, dark ocean.

He started off at a fair pace, giving out toys all over the galaxy. When he reached Mars, he pushed the transport button. Beeep! He waited a few seconds, but no toys appeared on the back of his sled. He tried the button again. Beeep! Still the back of his sled was empty. He was approaching the land of the Koos quite rapidly so he decided to come back to Mars after the other planets were done. Santa buckled his seat belt, pulled down his hat, and threw the throttle forward into light speed. In a second he saw millions of laughing Koos. They weren't even attacking, they were just staring wide-eyed at him. He was confused, until he heard a voice, "You've fallen right into my trap you silly little, or should I say big, fool!"

The next thing Santa knew he was in the bottom of a cold wet prison cell in the deepest part of the Koos' worst dungeon. He was alone, left to listen to the happy cries of the evil Koos. How could he escape those mangy, low down, rotten alien hooligans?

Back at Santa's workshop, the Elves had found Santa through the device on his sleigh. They were preparing for an emergency rescue, and even the reindeer were packing up their gear to go along. They decided to bring Santa's old sleigh in case his new one was no longer intact. The Elves had found out that the Koos had intercepted the toys while they were being zapped to Santa's sled. The Koos now had the toys and, worst of all, Santa. Was there any hope of saving Christmas? Well, even if there wasn't a chance to save Christmas, the Elves at least had to try. Besides, if the Elves were smart enough to teach reindeer to fly they were certainly clever enough to outsmart a few ignorant aliens.

When the Elves reached the land of the Koos, billions of little Koos shot out of a secret passage that led to the garage. Their quick little spaceships were not quick enough to catch the Elves or the reindeer though. One of the elves, whose name was Shubby Rotced, had a plan to capture the Koos. "We can use their own idea to trap them in the dungeon. If we fly right toward the border of Uranus, then pull up just before it, we can, hopefully, trap them in the prison cells of their own dungeon."

The other Elves nodded their heads. Soon the Koos were trapped in the dungeon, thanks to their own trap. But Santa and the toys still had not been recovered. What were they going to do? They had left the workshop with eight hours left in the night. Now there were only four. Surely they would need more time to rescue Santa and return the toys. It seemed as if there was no hope left. Then suddenly, out of the dark night of space flew, well, it appeared to be Santa! But how could this be the Santa from Earth, if the Santa from Earth was locked in the bottom of a cold, wet dungeon? It was a Santa from a nearby universe, and this Santa was the Santa from Earth's dad! This was all very confusing and hard for Santa's dad to say. But nobody cared. There might be a chance to save Christmas after all. With a twitch of the nose he had retrieved his son and the toys.

"Ho, ho, ho! Hi ya son." Santa exclaimed in a voice that was sure to be heard all over the universe. "Finished my route early, and I heard you were in a little predicament over here so I thought I'd stop on by and give you a hand. When you have eight hundred years of experience in a thing like this you tend to do things a little more hastily." The loud, gruff voice boomed loudly as he handed his son his bag of toys. Just as Santa was finished speaking, who should come zooming in on a space bike but old Yknaps, the King of the Babana Fruts.

"I too have come to help ya out Santy. In case those mean old Koos failed to cooperate and give back all of the toys I thought I'd bring you some of my own. All I've got is some rubber bananas that are dressed in pajamas, but hey, what do you expect from a group of aliens that evolved from bananas!"

When Santa, the one that Earthlings are most familiar with, was all packed up he jumped in his old sled, pulled by his good reindeer friends with only an hour to spare. Things were just like old times and now he was off to set things right.

Later that night, as The Great Santa Claus, as he was now called, sipped his hot cocoa, he thought how he had saved Christmas with only the help of a few pointy eared friends, some new gadgets, and dear old dad. He had delivered all of the presents to all of those joyful little aliens, even to Mars.

James Woods, Grade 6
Saint Joseph's School, West Saint Paul
Writer-in-Residence: John Coy

The Magical Dolphin

Introducer: Welcome, ladies and gentlemen to our play. And now "The Magical Dolphin!"

(Four large drum beats from the three male drummers)

Scene: A Girl *and a big* Snake *are in a beautiful part of the forest where many colorful flowers are blooming. The* Snake *slithers around the* Girl *and she is giggling as she looks at the snake.*

Snake: Are you hungry?
Girl: No.
Snake: Well I am.

(The Snake *slithers away, toward a group of* Weeds *(played by three girls). As he slithers, a maraca plays. The* Snake *wants to eat the* Weeds. *As he gets near them, they stand up, one of them shaking a tambourine, and they point at him.)*

The Weeds: Ahhhhhhhh!
Weed: Away, Snake!!

(He slithers away.)

Snake: What the heck? Well, I'm hungry.

(He slithers to them again. They stand again, tambourine shaking.)

The Weeds: Ahhhhhhhh!
Weed: Away, Snake!!

(He slithers away. Suddenly a Hunter *jumps out from behind some bushes. He is very excited.)*

Hunter: At last I've found you. I've waited all my life to catch you. Now die, sucker!

(Hunter *fires his rifle twice. Drums beat to the sound of the gun firing. The* Snake *falls dead. The* Hunter *runs over to him, walks around the* Snake *carefully, suspiciously. The* Hunter *leans down to listen to the* Snake's *heartbeat. The* Hunter *runs away, leaving the* Snake *there. The* Girl *enters and sees the* Snake *lying dead. She stands over him, and cries.)*

Girl: He was my friend. He was my friend.

(Slow, soft music plays from the xylophone. The Dolphin *enters, spinning slowly. She stops by the dead* Snake. *The* Weeds *begin to sing and stand up. The xylophone begins to play faster. The drums begin to beat faster and louder and louder. The* Dolphin *circles the* Snake *while sprinkling shiny stuff on him. The music is very loud and very fast. Suddenly the* Snake *cries out.)*

Snake: AHHHHH!

(All the music stops. The Snake *gets up. Silence. Then, with great joy, the* Snake *cries out:)*

Snake: I'M ALIVE!! I'M ALIVE!!

(The Snake *runs and dances around the stage shouting that he is alive. The slow xylophone plays as the* Dolphin *spins away, off stage.)*

Girl, Snake, Weeds: Thank you. . . . Thank you. . . .

(Drums play a dance beat and everyone dances with joy.)

Maria Taratsas & the "Bridges" class, Grade 3
Tri District Elementary School, Maplewood/Roseville/Saint Paul
Writer-in-Residence: Jaime Meyer

(excerpt from) Elevator Towns

1

A small red light suddenly changed green, and instantly a beat-up little yellow car lurched forward. It had been a good car, always getting the driver where he wanted to get to. Never once did the car ever go where it wanted to go. It was very unselfish in that sense. And the driver in the tattered front seat knew this fact very well. And as he switched gears, so as not to disrupt the flow of traffic, he whispered to his precious little yellow transportation.

"Just you and me, Suzy. No one else seems to understand but you and me." It went on like this for about 30 minutes. Driver and car united in mutual respect for one another.

"Why is it that no one else listens to me, Suzy? Do they think me snotty and arrogant? For they are surely very wrong if they do. I just seem to have a lot of facts to back me up. I don't think they want to recognize them. They don't want to refer to me as Related to Heaven. And why is that? Are they afraid that if they do, that I will send relatives after them? Are they afraid of me? Regardless, it's just you and me Suzy."

You see, Reginald Tupper V, the driver, was very unique in this world. And that prompted many people to tell him that he needed help, and that he was mentally ill. And for the past two years there had been just one thought in his head. But it was so unbelievable. You see, one day Reginald woke up and realized that it was Christmas. He had completely forgotten about it, so he scrambled out of bed to go shopping for a few select people. When he got out of the shower, he noticed that there were three visitors waiting for him. They were all dressed in party hats and holding a cake with 37 candles on it. Reginald then realized that December 25th was also his birthday. He was an incredibly forgetful person when it came to dates. Reginald was so terribly excited, because he didn't know anyone, and here were these three strangers throwing a party for him. It turns out that his lovely old grandmother had paid them to come over and cheer him up.

After the three visitors had gone home, Reginald had turned on his small black and white television only to find a man dressed up very nicely, preaching about someone called Jesus Christ.

"What a silly last name Christ is," Reginald said to himself. But as he continued to watch, he remembered from his old days back at Catholic school that Jesus' birthday was also on the 25th of December. Reginald thought it quite nice to have his birthday on the same day as a celebrity (after all, his name was being mentioned constantly on the television). So Reginald decided to read up on Jesus Christ, and find out all about him.

He read the Bible in just one week. And when he was finished, he was in complete and utter shock. For the pictures he had seen of Jesus showed him with dark hair, a scraggly beard, and a frail body. This was the very same description of Reginald. And then he remembered something very important.

"Our birthdays are both the 25th of December."

So Reginald was truly convinced that Jesus Christ was somehow his twin brother, and that they had somehow been separated a long, long time ago. He would tell everyone about this new phenomenon. People would have to respect him now; after all, Jesus Christ was a celebrity.

2

"OK, Suzy, we're here."

Reginald was now sprinting towards a huge hovering brick building. It had many doors and windows crammed into its concrete body. And under each door was a different title. This was the City Hall. Reginald had come here to make one final attempt to tell the mayor his "story" and get him to tell the rest of the town of its truth. He was incredibly nervous as he approached an old run down elevator that would surely lead him to his final destination. Reginald had always had a thing for elevators. They fascinated him. He could punch in any number and the elevator would take him to that floor without any hesitation. It was kind of like Suzy in that way. But the strange thing was, Reginald thought that everything about an elevator was a metaphor.

This was probably because when Reginald was five years old, his best friend, Jimmy, invited him to his birthday party. It just so happened that the party was being held at a Chinese restaurant. So

Reginald, Jimmy, and about four other boys, ate their meals, jabbering about their favorite super heroes and comic books, and having sword fights with their chopsticks. When they had finished, a lovely waitress in her late 20s brought them all fortune cookies. The waitress, whose name was Amber, was infertile, and would never have a child of her own. And so she was ecstatic to be serving the six boys. Amber loved children with all her heart, and was crushed to know that she would never have any of her own, since her husband refused to adopt. And actually, fortune cookies cost 25 cents apiece, but because she adored the boys so much, she gave the cookies to them for free. She always gave free fortune cookies to children.

These boys had never tried fortune cookies before, and sat in awe of the idea that messages could be hidden inside small morsels of food. They ripped open the cookies with ease and found small typed letters on very thin pieces of paper. Jimmy read his first and yelled it out loud.

"Love is in your future!"

"Oooohh! Jimmy's gonna get a GIRLFRIEND," chanted the rest of the boys.

Reginald was the last person to read.

"Pick a floor and let it lead you where you are to go," he muttered, "What does that mean?"

"Duh," Jimmy rang, "it's supposed to be a metaphor. Elevators are what you pick floors from. So elevators are the metaphor. It's saying that whatever elevators do, that they should be metaphors for your life."

And Reginald had certainly believed him. Every bit of it.

And as he was approaching this metaphorical elevator, a secretary all decked out in a white business suit hollered to him, "That one is jammed. It just stopped operating a couple of minutes ago. I haven't even had time to get an "Out Of Order" sign posted up. You can use the stairs though, they're just down the hall and to your left."

"Oh, that's all right, miss. The elevator is jammed. Can't you see? It's just another sign for me to get out of this blasted town."

Reginald was sprinting now, back to his lovely Suzy. He would get packed immediately and find some place far, far away. Anywhere would do, as long as it was far away. Reginald was convinced that anyone away from the City Hall would certainly believe him when he told them that Jesus Christ was his twin brother. He was convinced that it was just his town that was crazy, that every other town would surely be in awe of Reginald Tupper V, Jesus Christ's twin brother.

Aaron Mader, Grade 9
West Junior High School, Hopkins
Writer-in-Residence: Carol Dines

The Year That Flew By

I was in school one day and
I started to daydream. I had
lots of fun but when I woke
up everybody was gone. I waited
and waited some more. Then I looked
outside, it was summer vacation.
I couldn't believe it. I slept through
the year.

Jason Quiram, Grade 3
South Elementary School, Saint Peter
Writer-in-Residence: Dana Jensen

Fantasy

I am a child of imagination
my body is the sun
shining on the earth
my arms are the scales
of a double headed dragon
my legs are the ground
of the earth.
I am walking in the desert
when I see a man
he comes to me
he gives me something
it looks like a key
I unlock the door
and it leads to me.

Phillip Martini, Grade 5
Eisenhower Elementary School, Hopkins
Writer-in-Residence: Sheila O'Connor

AUTHOR INDEX

AUTHOR INDEX

AUTHOR INDEX

SCHOOL INDEX

SCHOOL INDEX

SCHOOL INDEX

PROGRAM WRITERS

Sigrid Bergie
John Coy
Florence Dacey
Carol Dines
Margot Fortunato Galt
Dana Jensen
Roseann Lloyd
Charlie Maguire
Jaime Meyer
John Minczeski
Sheila O'Connor
Stephen Peters
Jovelyn Richards
Richard Solly
Susan Marie Swanson
Diego Vazquez

THE LILLIAN WRIGHT AWARDS FOR CREATIVE WRITING

These awards are intended to recognize the finest literary achievements among young writers in Minnesota. The Wright Awards are underwritten by the **Lillian Wright and C. Emil Berglund Foundation**. Award winners from *A Special Stretch of Sky* will be announced at the December 1997 Publication Celebration, and subsequently listed in next year's Anthology. The judge of the 1996-97 Awards is Helen McLean, longtime teacher in the Saint Paul Public Schools, past participant in the COMPAS Dialogue Program, and current member of the Writers & Artists in the Schools Advisory Committee.

On this page, COMPAS is proud to honor the winners of the third annual Lillian Wright Awards for Creative Writing, given to the best examples of student writing featured in the 1995-96 COMPAS Writers & Artists in the Schools anthology, *Rooftop Jailbirds*. The 1995-96 winners are:

BEST SONG in GRADES K-12:
"State Fair," by the 4th Grade Core Group
Richardson Elementary School, North Saint Paul.

BEST POETRY in GRADES K-3:
"Emily" by Amy Jansen
Grade 3, South Elementary School, Saint Peter.

[Due to the large number of entries, two selections were made in the following category.]
BEST POETRY in GRADES 4-6:
"My Love for My Mom," by Poul Pedersen
Grade 6, Eisenhower Elementary School, Hopkins.

BEST POETRY in GRADES 4-6:
"Beginning of Spring," by Jeffery Niesen
Grade 4, Grey Cloud Elementary School, Cottage Grove.

BEST POETRY in GRADES 7-8:
"Who I Am," by Meredith Reiches
Grade 7, Blake Middle School, Hopkins.

BEST POETRY in GRADES 9-12:
"Mommy Got the Yellow Car, Daddy Got the Black One,"
by Caitlin Williams, Grade 9, South View Middle School, Edina.

BEST PROSE in GRADES K-6:
"Untitled," by Emily Jacobsen
Grade 5, Chelsea Heights Elementary School, Saint Paul.

BEST PROSE in GRADES 7-12:
"Before You Were Born," by Candice So
Grade 12, Mayo High School, Rochester.

AWARDS JUDGE: Catherine Barner, former English teacher at Battle Lake High School, and longtime Contact Teacher and supporter of the Writers & Artists in the Schools program.